READING GROUP CHOICES

2016

*Selections for lively
book discussions*

Reading Group Choices' goal is to join with publishers, bookstores, libraries, trade associations, and authors to develop resources to enhance the shared reading group experience. *Reading Group Choices* is distributed annually to bookstores, libraries, and directly to book groups. Titles from previous issues are posted on ReadingGroupChoices.com. Books presented here have been recommended by book group members, librarians, booksellers, literary agents, publicists, authors, and publishers. All submissions are then reviewed to ensure the discussibility of each title. Once a title is approved for inclusion, publishers are asked to underwrite production costs, so that copies of *Reading Group Choices* can be distributed for a minimal charge. For additional copies, please call your local library or bookstore, or contact us. Quantities are limited. For more information, please visit our website at **ReadingGroupChoices.com.**

Cover art, *Girl Reading #2* by Sophie Blackall [2015].

Copyright © 2015 Reading Group Choices LLC

All Rights Reserved.

Published in the United States by Reading Group Choices LLC

ISBN 9780990689928

For further information, contact:
Reading Group Choices
info@ReadingGroupChoices.com
ReadingGroupChoices.com

PRAISE FOR *READING GROUP CHOICES*

"We have learned over the years that displays are a great way to encourage circulation at our small, rural library. One of our best displays is based on the wonderful literary guide published by Reading Group Choices! . . . Patrons cannot wait to get their copies and start reading. We sincerely LOVE your product and feel that it helps us create one of our favorite displays EVER."
—**Gail Nartker, Sandusky District Library**

"Reading Group Choices continues to be a first-rate guide for those delicious reads that book group members enjoy reading, and that prompt the most enriching discussions." —**Donna Paz Kaufman, Paz & Associates, The Bookstore Training Group**

"I recommend Reading Group Choices as the number one starting point for book clubs. The newsletter is fantastic and I especially like the Spotlight Book Club section. It is a nice way to meet other book clubs. I am very happy with the book selections offered by Reading Group Choices. Thank you for this excellent service." —**Ana Martin, Cover to Cover Book Club, Hollywood, FL**

"Not only is Reading Group Choices a great resource for individual readers and book groups, it's also an invaluable tool for teachers looking to introduce new books into their curriculum. Reading Group Choices is a brilliant concept, well executed." —**Kathleen Rourke, Executive Director of Educational Sales and Marketing, Candlewick Press**

"I love your book, website and the newsletters! As an organizer of two book clubs, it's so great to get an early line on upcoming titles. The hardest part is waiting so long to read the book! By using recommendations from your newsletters, I can build a list of monthly book selections one whole year in advance." —**Marcia, CCSI Book Club**

"I sat down and read the new "Choices" cover to cover and liked it very much. I think you did a terrific job. We've already started handing out a book to each book club as we speak to them (several a week)."
—**Nancy Olson, former owner, Quail Ridge Books & Music**

Welcome to
READING GROUP
Choices

A book is not complete until it's read. The reader's mind flows through sentences as through a circuit – it illuminates them and brings them to life.

—**E.L. Doctorow** (1931-2015)

Dear Readers,

Welcome to the 22nd edition of Reading Group Choices. We hope the books and conversation starters included in this collection inspire meaningful and lively discussions!

Over the past year, we received many requests and suggestions from our reading groups, and we listened. We have added Young Adult book recommendations to our website and monthly eNewsletter. We have also added more nonfiction recommendations, book pairings, and themed book lists. We are continuing to host events for reading groups at bookstores and book festivals around the country, and we list upcoming dates in our monthly newsletters.

The 2016 edition not only provides over 75 book recommendations, but it offers three sections: fiction, nonfiction, and young adult. There are books by authors and publishers you will recognize as well as books by debut authors and independent presses from California to Colorado to New York. There are translated works, memoirs (including a graphic novel memoir), and some books that will be published in 2016, so when you plan your group's list for the year, you can plan ahead!

Many of the books included in this edition will also be included in contests on our website this fall and winter so be sure to check the site on the first of each month, and to sign up for our monthly eNewsletter to find out what's new!

As always, thank you to our readers for supporting and inspiring us. Thank you as well to our authors, our independent bookstores, and our friends in publishing.

Please visit us online at ReadingGroupChoices.com, like us on Facebook, and find us on Twitter and through our mobile app. To order more copies of this edition, or any of our past editions, you can fill out the order form at the back of this book, or visit our online store on our website.

Here's to another year of happy reading!

M. m

Mary Morgan
Reading Group Choices

Contents

FICTION

ALL THE SINGLE LADIES
Dorothea Benton Frank

The perennial *New York Times* bestselling author returns with an emotionally resonant novel that illuminates the power of friendship in women's lives, and is filled with her trademark wit, poignant and timely themes, sassy, flesh-and-blood characters, and the steamy Southern atmosphere and beauty of her beloved Carolina Lowcountry.

Few writers capture the complexities, pain, and joy of relationships—between friends, family members, husbands and wives, or lovers—as beloved *New York Times* bestselling author Dorothea Benton Frank. In this charming, evocative, soul-touching novel, she once again takes us deep into the heart of the magical Lowcountry where three amazing middle-aged women are bonded by another amazing woman's death.

Through their shared loss they forge a deep friendship, asking critical questions. Who was their friend and what did her life mean? Are they living the lives they imagined for themselves? Will they ever be able to afford to retire? How will they maximize their happiness? Security? Health? And ultimately, their own legacies?

A plan is conceived and unfurls with each turn of the tide during one sweltering summer on the Isle of Palms. Without ever fully realizing how close they were to the edge, they finally triumph amid laughter and maybe even newfound love.

"All the Single Ladies is vintage Dorothea Benton Frank - a funny, poignant read." —**Liane Moriarty, #1** *New York Times* **Bestselling author of** *Big Little Lies and The Husband's Secret*

ABOUT THE AUTHOR: *New York Times* bestselling author **Dorothea Benton Frank** was born and raised on Sullivans Island, South Carolina. She resides in the New York area with her husband.

June 2015 | Hardcover | Fiction | 368 pp | $26.99 | ISBN 9780062132567
William Morrow | harpercollins.com | dotfrank.com

CONVERSATION STARTERS

1. One important issue in the book is how these women have reached a point in their lives where they probably expected to have a secure future, but because of unforeseen circumstances they don't. How does this impact the plot? Their choices?

2. What is your opinion concerning the legalization of marijuana? If you are opposed to it, do you feel differently regarding medical use to alleviate pain for certain individuals? How would you feel if your child's career was based on something you could not ethically support?

3. Despite Carrie and Suzanne's devoted friendship to Kathy Harper, there was a lot about her life she hadn't shared. Were you surprised by how much they didn't know about her?

4. What is your interpretation of the Emily Dickinson poem at the start of the book and how it relates to *All the Single Ladies*?

5. In the beginning of the book, Lisa respects but isn't overly fond of Dr. Harry Black. In fact, she refers to him as Darth Vader. As he begins to court Suzanne, however, she gets to see his other sides. Carrie and Suzanne did the same thing with Paul. Would you say they were all too quick to judge?

6. Arthur Aron's 36 questions are from an actual study undertaken by this prominent psychologist. Do you think it makes sense to bring out the 36 questions at the start of a blossoming relationship? Do you think it could rush intimacy or create a false sense of closeness? Would you try it?

7. If, knowing where their paths are headed at the end of the book, you could step into the shoes of one character --- Suzanne's, Lisa's, Carrie's or Miss Trudie's --- which ones would you wear and why?

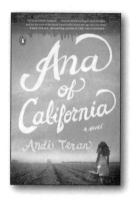

ANA OF CALIFORNIA
Andi Teran

In the grand tradition of *Anne of Green Gables*, *Bridget Jones's Diary*, and *The Three Weissmanns of Westport*, Andi Teran's captivating debut novel offers a contemporary twist on a beloved classic. Fifteen-year-old orphan Ana Cortez has just blown her last chance with a foster family. It's a group home next—unless she agrees to leave East Los Angeles for a farm trainee program in Northern California.

When she first arrives, Ana can't tell a tomato plant from a blackberry bush, and Emmett Garber is skeptical that this slight city girl can be any help on his farm. His sister Abbie, however, thinks Ana might be just what they need. Ana comes to love Garber Farm, and even Emmett has to admit that her hard work is an asset. But when she inadvertently stirs up trouble in town, Ana is afraid she might have ruined her last chance at finding a place to belong.

"Andi Teran's first novel is vivid and fully realized, an entire universe expertly condensed into the pages you hold in your hands. Ana herself is a complicated delight, and by the end of the book I wanted to scoop her up into my arms." —**New York Times bestselling author Emma Straub**

"Anne of Green Gables fans will rejoice; newcomers will find a satisfying tale; and Ana's high jinx will leave both types of readers smiling and asking for more." —***Kirkus Reviews***

ABOUT THE AUTHOR: **Andi Teran** is from El Paso, Texas. She has written about fashion, film, and culture for *Vanity Fair*, *Monocle*, *New York Magazine*, and MTV. She currently resides in Los Angeles. *Ana of California* is her first novel.

June 2015 | Trade Paperback | Fiction | 368 pp | $16.00 | ISBN 9780143126492
Penguin Books | penguinrandomhouse.com | anditeran.com

CONVERSATION STARTERS

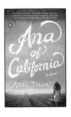

1. Lupe Saucedo knows that Ana's last foster situation was far from ideal, but she's unable to place her with another family. Should Lupe have taken Ana in herself? Does Lupe have Ana's best interests at heart?

2. On the ride home from the airport, Emmett warms to Ana after learning that she likes Neil Young. Later, Ana and Rye bond over their shared love of the band Hex. Music can be a powerful force that brings strangers together. Why might this be?

3. Why is Abbie so nervous when Ana arrives at the farm? Should Abbie have told Ana about Josie and why she left in order to prevent future misunderstandings?

4. What does Miranda's mistake about "Mexican Coke" say about her? Do Miranda's later actions redeem her initial treatment of Ana?

5. Ana's parents were gang members who were involved in illegal activities and eventually murdered by a rival gang. Even though Ana was just a young child, she fears that prison—or worse—is her "destiny." How do kids like Ana come to believe that they are criminals without even committing a crime?

6. Once the school year starts, Ana, Rye, and Brady are harassed by some of the popular kids and eat lunch together at "the official weirdo table" (p. 196). How well does the author capture the realities of being a teenager?

7. When Vic, Rolo, and Rene are tempted to leave the Garbers and begin working at the Keyserville farm for higher pay, it's Ana who convinces them to stay. Besides helping Emmett pay their full wages, how does Ana persuade them to change their minds?

8. Why does Abbie find it so difficult to believe that Will is interested in her romantically? Would their ages make any difference if Will were the older of the two?

9. What are some ways in which Ana is similar to the heroine of *Anne of Green Gables*? What are some ways in which she's different?

10. Besides Ana, who is your favorite character? What is it about him or her that appeals to you?

AND THE DARK SACRED NIGHT
Julia Glass

Kit Noonan is an unemployed art historian with twins to help support and a mortgage to pay—and a wife frustrated by his inertia. Raised by a strong-willed, secretive single mother, Kit has never known the identity of his father—a mystery that his wife insists he must solve to move forward with his life. Out of desperation, Kit goes to the mountain retreat of his mother's former husband, Jasper, a take-no-prisoners outdoorsman. There, in the midst of a fierce blizzard, Kit and Jasper confront memories of the bittersweet decade when their families were joined. Reluctantly breaking a long-ago promise, Jasper connects Kit with Lucinda and Zeke Burns, who know the answer he's looking for. Readers of Glass's first novel, *Three Junes*, will recognize Lucinda as the mother of Malachy, the music critic who died of AIDS. In fact, to fully understand the secrets surrounding his paternity, Kit will travel farther still, meeting Fenno McLeod, now in his late fifties, and Fenno's longtime companion, the gregarious Walter Kinderman.

*An elegant and moving novel." —**The New Yorker***

*"A tender, insightful, and winning exploration of the modern family and the infinite number of shapes it can take." —**People***

*"Sophisticated and surprising. . . . Luminous." —**San Francisco Chronicle***

*"The only regret you'll have at the end of this particular story is that it's over." —**Entertainment Weekly***

ABOUT THE AUTHOR: **Julia Glass** is the author of *Three Junes*, winner of the 2002 National Book Award for Fiction; *The Whole World Over*; *I See You Everywhere*, winner of the 2009 Binghamton University John Gardner Book Award; and *The Widower's Tale*. Her personal essays have been widely anthologized. A recipient of fellowships from the National Endowment for the Arts, the New York Foundation for the Arts, and the Radcliffe Institute for Advanced Study, Glass also teaches fiction writing, most frequently at the Fine Arts Center in Provincetown. She lives with her family in Marblehead, Massachusetts.

January 2015 | Trade Paperback | Fiction | 400 pp | $15.95 | ISBN 9780307456113
Anchor | penguinrandomhouse.com

CONVERSATION STARTERS

1. Kit's wife, Sandra, tells him, "I think you need to move, I mean pry yourself free from a place that's become so familiar you simply can't see it" (p. 22). Have you ever come to a place in your life where you felt stuck? How did you resolve this?

2. Why do you think Daphne insists on keeping the name of Kit's father a secret? Whom is she protecting?

3. If you were Kit, do you think you could/would have waited so long to find your father? Do you think men and women have different attitudes toward "finding" their lost family connections?

4. Describe Kit and Daphne's relationship. How does this change throughout the book?

5. Daphne accepted Lucinda's help with Kit for the first few years of his life. What do you think about her cutting off that connection so abruptly? Can you empathize with her reasons for doing so?

6. Lucinda has yearned for decades to reconnect with Kit. Do you think she should have done that on her own, without waiting for him to take the initiative? Or do you think the initiative always has to come from the child/grandchild?

7. Did you have a magical time or place in your life similar to that summer?

8. In your view, who has the most to forgive? Who most deserves forgiveness? Who most needs it?

9. Lucinda gets mad at Zeke for hiding Malachy's need to know of Kit, and gets mad at Jonathan for hiding his homosexuality from Malachy as well as from his parents. Do you think these secrets were justified?

10. The Burnses' barn, the Shed at the music camp, Jasper's crow's nest: All of these structures hold meaning for the characters involved. Are there places in your life that you feel as strongly about?

11. In the end, do you think Kit found what he was looking for?

12. What character in this story do you most identify with, and why?

THE ART OF CRASH LANDING
Melissa DeCarlo

Broke and knocked up, Mattie Wallace has got all her worldly possessions crammed into six giant trash bags and nowhere to go. Try as she might, she really is turning into her late mother, a broken alcoholic who never met a bad choice she didn't make.

When Mattie gets news of a possible inheritance left by a grandmother she's never met, she jumps at this one last chance to turn things around. Leaving the Florida Panhandle, she drives eight hundred miles to her mother's birthplace—the tiny town of Gandy, Oklahoma. There, she soon learns that her mother remains a local mystery—a happy, talented teenager who inexplicably skipped town thirty-five years ago with nothing but the clothes on her back. But the girl they describe bears little resemblance to the damaged woman Mattie knew, and before long it becomes clear that something terrible happened to her mother. The deeper Mattie digs for answers, the more precarious her situation becomes. Giving up, however, isn't an option. Uncovering what started her mother's downward spiral might be the only way to stop her own.

"DeCarlo's debut is confident and accomplished, filled with heart and humor." —*Kirkus*

"Full of heart and sass. . . . This is a sparkling, funny, and moving debut." —**Edan Lepucki, author of** *California*

"A dazzling debut that truly soars, about figuring out the tug of the past, about family mysteries and the marvels of forgiveness, and all of it features a spunky heroine readers won't be able to stop falling in love with." —**Caroline Leavitt, author of** *Is This Tomorrow and Pictures of You*

About the Author: **Melissa DeCarlo** was born and raised in Oklahoma City, and has worked as an artist, graphic designer, grant writer, and even (back when computers were the size of refrigerators) a computer programmer. *The Art of Crash Landing* is her first novel. Melissa now lives in East Texas with her husband and a motley crew of rescue animals.

September 2015 | Trade Paperback | Fiction | 432 pp | $15.99 | ISBN 9780062390547
Harper Paperbacks | harpercollins.com | melissadecarlo.com

CONVERSATION STARTERS

1. Early on in the book it becomes clear that Mattie has a long history of making bad decisions. Do any of the other characters make self-destructive choices in their lives? How have those choices shaped present circumstances?

2. Even though Queeg was only Mattie's stepfather for three years, it's obvious they're still close. Why do you think Mattie maintained a close relationship with Queeg? Are there relationships from your past that you're surprised you've maintained? Some you're surprised you've let go?

3. Part of the reason Mattie finds Tawny annoying is how much the girl reminds Mattie of herself as a teenager. If you could meet your teenaged self, what advice would you give?

4. Even thirty-five years later, Karleen still harbors strong feelings about Genie. Why do you think the dynamic between them changes when Genie goes off to college? How does that reflect the evolution of friendships over time?

5. As she investigates her mother's history, Mattie's own past and her relationship with her mother are revealed one piece at a time. As you progressed through the book, how did your feelings toward Mattie change? What about your feelings toward her mother?

6. The two settings in the book are the Florida panhandle with its beaches and seagulls, and a small town in Oklahoma with its wind and storms. Do you think the settings were important to the story? Why or why not?

7. What was the emotional significance of the old Malibu to Genie and to Mattie? Do you have anything you've held onto longer than you should because of the memories tied to it? What would it take for you to let it go?

8. The ability or inability to let go of guilt and move on with life is a recurring theme in this novel. What are some of the characters whose stories reflect this theme, and how did they deal with (or not deal with) their guilt? How common is it for people to harbor guilt that holds them back?

9. If you could check back in with Mattie a year after the book's ending, what do you think you'd find? What do you wish you'd find? Are the answers to those two questions the same or different?

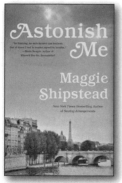

ASTONISH ME
Maggie Shipstead

From the author of the widely acclaimed debut novel *Seating Arrangements*, winner of the Dylan Thomas Prize and the *Los Angeles Times* Book Prize for First Fiction: a gorgeously written, fiercely compelling glimpse into the passionate, political world of professional ballet and its magnetic hold over two generations.

Astonish Me is the irresistible story of Joan, a ballerina whose life has been shaped by her relationship with the world-famous dancer Arslan Rusakov, whom she helps defect from the Soviet Union to the United States. While Arslan's career takes off in New York, Joan's slowly declines, ending when she becomes pregnant and decides to marry her longtime admirer, a PhD student named Jacob. As the years pass, Joan settles into her new life in California, teaching dance and watching her son, Harry, become a ballet prodigy himself. But when Harry's success brings him into close contact with Arslan, explosive secrets are revealed that shatter the delicate balance Joan has struck between her past and present.

In graceful, inimitable prose, Shipstead draws us into an extraordinary world and into the lives of her vivid and tempestuous characters. Filled with intrigue, brilliant satire, and emotional nuance, *Astonish Me* is a superlative follow-up to Shipstead's superb debut.

"So dazzling, so sure-handed and fearless, that at times I had to remind myself to breathe." —**Maria Semple, author of *Where'd You Go, Bernadette***

"A novel you must read." —**Ron Charles, *The Washington Post***

"A breathtaking work of art." —**O, *The Oprah Magazine***

"Precise . . . Flawless . . . Transcendent." —**Maureen Corrigan, NPR**

ABOUT THE AUTHOR: **Maggie Shipstead** is a graduate of the Iowa Writers' Workshop and a former Wallace Stegner Fellow at Stanford University. Her first novel, *Seating Arrangements*, was a *New York Times* best seller, a finalist for the Flaherty-Dunnan First Novel Prize, and the winner of the Dylan Thomas Prize and the *Los Angeles Times* Book Prize for First Fiction.

January 2015 | Trade Paperback | Fiction | 272 pp | $15.00 | ISBN 9780345804617
Vintage | penguinrandomhouse.com | maggieshipstead.com

CONVERSATION STARTERS

1. What does "Astonish me" mean, as a metaphor in the novel?

2. Who is the main character? Is that person also the hero?

3. Shipstead skips forward and backward in time throughout the novel. How does she use these leaps to fill in the story?

4. "Elaine ingests a steady but restricted diet of cocaine without apparent consequence. The key, she has said to Joan, is control. Control is the key to everything." (page 8) What does Elaine mean by "control"? Which characters in the novel lose control, and to what effect?

5. And how does the perfectionism required of ballet dancers play into intent and control?

6. Is Joan's aggressive pursuit of Arslan out of character for her? Why does she do it?

7. Throughout the novel, characters wonder why Arslan chose Joan to help him defect. Why do you think he chose her?

8. How does Sandy shape her daughter's future? What effect does her behavior at Disneyland have?

9. "I think things can be true even if they didn't really happen," Jacob says on page 144. What does he mean by this? How does it play out in his family's life?

10. Jacob adored Joan from childhood; Harry adored Chloe from childhood. How else does the younger generation resemble the older one? How do they differ?

11. Why do Harry's feelings for Chloe change?

12. What does "parent" mean, in terms of the novel? Which characters make good parents?

13. What is the metaphor of Emma Livry, the ballet dancer whose tutu catches fire?

14. What does Rodina, the title of Arslan and Chloe's ballet, mean? (In Russia, it refers to "motherland.")

15. Do you think Jacob decides to stay through the end of the performance?

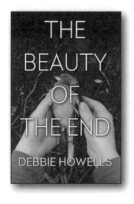

THE BEAUTY OF THE END
Debbie Howells

From the acclaimed author of *The Bones of You* comes a haunting and heartbreaking new psychological thriller that is both a masterpiece of suspense and a powerful rumination on lost love.

"I was fourteen when I fell in love with a goddess..."

So begins the testimony of Noah Calaway, an ex-lawyer with a sideline in armchair criminal psychology. Now living an aimless life in an inherited cottage in the English countryside, Noah is haunted by the memory of the beguiling young woman who left him at the altar sixteen years earlier. Then one day he receives a troubling phone call. April, the woman he once loved, lies in a coma, the victim of an apparent overdose—and the lead suspect in the brutal murder of her stepfather. Deep in his bones, Noah believes that April is innocent. Then again, he also believed they would spend the rest of their lives together.

While Noah searches for evidence that will clear April's name, a teenager named Ella begins to sift through the secrets of her own painful family history. The same age as April was when Noah first met her, Ella harbours a revelation that could be the key to solving the murder. As the two stories converge, there are shocking consequences when at last, the truth emerges.

Or so everyone believes...

"Dynamic, haunting and complex...compared to The Lovely Bones.*"*
—*Library Journal*

"One of those books that captivates you from the first page and never lets go. I savored every word. Truly brilliant!"—**Lisa Jackson, #1 *New York Times* bestselling author**

ABOUT THE AUTHOR: **Debbie Howells** is the author of *The Bones of You*, her debut thriller which sold internationally for six-figures in several countries. She lives in West Sussex with her family; visit her online at DebbieHowells.com.

July 2016 | Hardcover | Fiction | 320 pp | $25.00 | ISBN 9781496705983
Kensington | kensingtonbooks.com | debbiehowells.com

CONVERSATION STARTERS

1. As the story opens, even with evidence to the contrary, Noah is convinced of April's innocence. As a reader, do you agree with him? Can we ever be so sure about someone, even when we know them very well?

2. Even as a young man, Will's behavior could be seen as self-interested. This is more apparent when you learn how he is as an adult. Would you describe him as narcissistic? Is human behaviour ever entirely unselfish?

3. Ella's discovery of her past is extremely distressing for her. How better could her parents have prepared her, or would it have been easier for her never to have found out the truth?

4. Was Noah the best person to represent April? Did his belief in her help or hinder his investigation? Would an outsider have been more able to uncover the truth?

5. We often base our assessment of people on first impressions, and form strong opinions about those we've known a long time. How easy is it to discard such beliefs and consider what might seem unbelievable?

6. How do you think Noah's personality influenced his investigation? Did his relationship with Will affect his judgment?

7. Is Bea's distrust of Noah justified? Has your own opinion of someone ever been swayed—wrongly—by that of a convincing other?

8. Could Noah's behaviour be seen as self-destructive, even if ultimately, it led to him to change himself for the better?

9. A central theme of the story is the issue of assisted dying versus preserving life at all costs. How did April's actions affect other characters on both sides of this issue?

10. Why do you think Noah never gave up on April? Can you relate that to your own life in any way?

BEST BOY
Eli Gottlieb

For fans of *The Curious Incident of the Dog in the Night-Time* comes this landmark novel about autism, memory, and, ultimately, redemption.

Sent to a "therapeutic community" for autism at the age of eleven, Todd Aaron, now in his fifties, is the "Old Fox" of Payton LivingCenter. A joyous man who rereads the encyclopedia compulsively, he is unnerved by the sudden arrivals of a menacing new staffer and a disruptive, brain-injured roommate. His equilibrium is further worsened by Martine, a one-eyed new resident who has romantic intentions and convinces him to go off his meds to feel "normal" again. Undone by these pressures, Todd attempts an escape to return "home" to his younger brother and to a childhood that now inhabits only his dreams. Written astonishingly in the first-person voice of an autistic, adult man, *Best Boy* is a piercing, achingly funny, finally shattering novel no reader can ever forget.

"Gottlieb's marvelous novel has happened so that readers may be in awe of all the universe's creations."—**Booklist** (starred review)

"[An] eloquent, sensitive rendering of a marginalized life...Gottlieb merits praise for both the endearing eloquence of Todd's voice and a deeply sympathetic parable that speaks to a time when rising autism rates and long-lived elders force many to weigh tough options."—**Kirkus Reviews** (starred review)

"The story will appeal to a very broad range of readers: . . . Gottlieb's attention to crafting Todd's internal monologue is something to behold."
—**Publishers Weekly** (starred review)

Gottlieb has created something quite exceptional in [Todd Aaron] . . . A deeply moving portrait of a kind and gentle soul. Recommended for all readers."—**Library Journal** (starred review)

ABOUT THE AUTHOR: **Eli Gottlieb** is the author of *Best Boy*, among other novels. His works have been translated into a dozen languages. He lives in New York City.

August 2015 | Hardcover | Fiction | 256 pp | $24.95 | ISBN 978163149047
Liveright | wwnorton.com | eligottlieb.com

CONVERSATION STARTERS

1. What is the significance of the book's title? How does being a 'best boy' shape Todd's identity and development?

2. Discuss Todd's relationship with his family. How do they deal with his disability?

3. Do you think it was fair of Todd's mother to send him away to so many institutions?

4. What role do Nate and his family play in Todd's life?

5. How does Nate change throughout the story? In your opinion, was he a likeable character? Would you have acted differently in his situation?

6. Discuss the significance of Todd's stick in the woods. What purpose does it serve in the story?

7. Discuss the significance of the encyclopedia ("Mr. B").

8. In Chapter 17, Todd recalls an incident that happened several years ago with Nate's family. Beth had asked Todd to watch her sons at the restaurant while she stepped out for a phone call, and while Todd wasn't paying attention the boys run onto the street and cause a car crash. Nate asks Beth, "You left *him* in charge?" Do you think it was Beth's fault? How does this incident affect their relationship with Todd?

9. What scene did you find most poignant?

10. What events from Todd's early childhood do you believe were most instrumental (or detrimental) to his development?

11. Do you think that Martine's influence on Todd was positive or negative? Do you think it was right for Martine to convince Todd to go off of his medication?

12. What were your thoughts on the ending of the book? Do you feel hopeful for Todd's future?

13. There are many things still unknown about autism, which is said to be "the largest childhood epidemic in history" (181). According to Todd, "The spectrum is so wide that actually almost anyone can be on it" (183). Did reading the novel alter your view on autism? Did it change your thoughts about mental institutions?

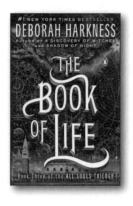

THE BOOK OF LIFE
Deborah Harkness

The #1 *New York Times* bestselling series finale and sequel to *A Discovery of Witches* and *Shadow of Night*

Fans of the All Souls Trilogy sent this highly anticipated finale straight to #1 on the *New York Times* hardcover bestseller list. Bringing the series' magic and suspense to a deeply satisfying conclusion, *The Book of Life* is poised to become an even bigger phenomenon in paperback.

Diana and Matthew time-travel back from Elizabethan London to make a dramatic return to the present—facing new crises and old enemies. At Matthew's ancestral home, Sept-Tours, they reunite with the beloved cast of characters from *A Discovery of Witches*—with one significant exception. But the real threat to their future has yet to be revealed, and when it is, the search for Ashmole 782 and its missing pages takes on even more urgency.

*"Harkness has immersed and spellbound readers with her alternative universe. . . . Her ambitious melding of scientific and historical detail is inventive and brings surprising depth. . . . The Book of Life brims with sensuality, intrigue, violence and much-welcome humor." —**Los Angeles Times***

ABOUT THE AUTHOR: **Deborah Harkness** is the #1 *New York Times*–bestselling author of *A Discovery of Witches* and *Shadow of Night*, the first two volumes in the All Souls Trilogy. She lives in Los Angeles.

May 2015 | Trade Paperback | Fiction | 576 pp | $17.00 | ISBN 9780143127529
Penguin Books | penguinrandomhouse.com | deborahharkness.com

CONVERSATION STARTERS

1. Throughout *The Book of Life*, the ghosts of Philippe de Clermont and Emily Mather observe what their loved ones are doing in the world of the living. Have you ever felt the protective presence of friends or family who have passed on?

2. Although we don't meet Matthew's nephew Gallowglass until *Shadow of the Night*, we learn that—under orders from Philippe—he has been protecting Diana from afar since she was born. We also learn that Gallowglass has fallen deeply in love with Diana. How did this knowledge affect your opinion of him? Are there ways in which he might have made Diana a better mate than Matthew?

3. Matthew's centuries-old decision to let Benjamin live set in motion a chain of events that threatens Diana as well as their newborn twins. To what extent is Matthew responsible for the suffering that Benjamin has caused?

4. Several characters from earlier in the series return to play a part in the final volume, including Jack, Father Hubbard, and Timothy Weston—the daemon from the Bodleian. Whose reappearance astonished you the most? Whose absence did you find most painful?

5. Matthew deliberately walks into Benjamin's trap, initiating the Queen's Gambit, a chess move that he habitually avoids in order to protect his queen. In this case, he puts his queen—Diana—into play against Benjamin. Were you surprised by Matthew's decision? Would it have been possible to overcome Benjamin if Matthew hadn't allowed Diana to risk her life?

6. The de Clermonts eventually discover that Gerbert—the vampire who led the congregation in denouncing Matthew and Diana's relationships—had himself been consorting with witches and daemons for centuries. Unfortunately, the news is full of illegal and often hypocritical acts committed by people in positions of power. Do you think that it's power that corrupts, or are the corrupt more inclined than most to seek power?

7. What do you think the future holds for Matthew and Diana? Which characters from the series would you like to have learned more about?

THE BOOK OF UNKNOWN AMERICANS

Cristina Henríquez

New York Times and Washington Post Notable Book, NPR Great Read, and Oprah.com, *School Library Journal*, and *BookPage* Best Book of the Year

Arturo and Alma Rivera have lived their whole lives in Mexico. One day, their beautiful fifteen-year-old daughter, Maribel, sustains a terrible injury, one that casts doubt on whether she'll ever be the same. And so, leaving all they have behind, the Riveras come to America with a single dream: that in this country of great opportunity and resources, Maribel can get better.

When Mayor Toro, whose family is from Panama, sees Maribel in a Dollar Tree store, it is love at first sight. It's also the beginning of a friendship between the Rivera and Toro families, whose web of guilt and love and responsibility is at this novel's core.

Woven into their stories are the testimonials of men and women who have come to the United States from all over Latin America. Their journeys and their voices will inspire you, surprise you, and break your heart.

Suspenseful, wry and immediate, rich in spirit and humanity, *The Book of Unknown Americans* is a work of rare force and originality that offers a resonant new definition of what it means to be an American.

"Vivid . . . . Striking. . . . A ringing paean to love in general: to the love between man and wife, parent and child, outsider and newcomer, pilgrims and promised land." —**The Washington Post**

"Powerful. . . . Moving. . . . [Henríquez has] myriad gifts as a writer." —**The New York Times**

About the Author: Cristina Henríquez is the author of the story collection *Come Together, Fall Apart*, which was a *New York Times* Editors' Choice selection, and the novel *The World in Half*. Her work has appeared in *The New Yorker*, *The Atlantic*, *The American Scholar*, *Glimmer Train*, the *Virginia Quarterly Review*, *Ploughshares*, *TriQuarterly*, *AGNI*, and *Oxford American*, as well as in various anthologies. She lives in Illinois.

March 2015 | Trade Paperback | Fiction | 304 pp | $14.95 | ISBN 9780345806406
Vintage | penguinrandomhouse.com | cristinahenriquez.com

CONVERSATION STARTERS

1. How does Alma's perspective in the novel's first chapter illustrate her and her family's hopes for their new life in America? Take another look at her statement after the trip to the gas station: "The three of us started toward the road, doubling back in the direction from which we had come, heading toward home" (11). What are the meanings of "home" here, and how does this scene show how America meets and differs from the Riveras' expectations of it?

2. Mayor describes how he's bullied at school and his general feelings of not fitting in. How do you think this draws him to Maribel? What do they have in common that perhaps those around them, including their parents, cannot see on the surface?

3. What are some key differences in the way that the women in the novel respond to challenges of assimilation compared to the men? How does Alma's point of view highlight these differences?

4. What brings Alma and Celia together as neighbors and friends, and how does their relationship change by the end of the book?

5. How does Alma's lingering guilt about Maribel's accident affect her choices and interactions when she's in America? Do you think that she still feels this way by the end of the book? What does she have to do, and realize within herself, to move beyond her feelings?

6. Discuss Quisqueya's role in what happens to Mayor and Maribel. Without her intervention, how might have their relationship, and ultimately the novel, ended differently?

7. How does the Toros' buying a car influence the course of events in the novel? What does the car mean for Rafael and Mayor individually and for their father-son relationship?

8. Do you, the members of your family, or your friends have stories of moving to another country to start a new life? Did any of the stories in the novel resonate with those you know?

9. How does the final chapter, told in Arturo's voice, influence your understanding of what he felt about America? What do you make of how he ends his narrative, "I loved this country," and that it is the last line of the book (286)?

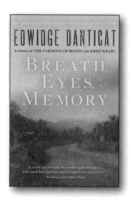

Breath, Eyes, Memory
Edwidge Danticat

The 20th anniversary edition of Edwidge Danticat's groundbreaking debut—now an established classic—revised and with a new introduction by the author, and including extensive bonus materials.

At the age of twelve, Sophie Caco is sent from her impoverished Haitian village to New York to be reunited with a mother she barely remembers. There she discovers secrets that no child should ever know, and a legacy of shame that can be healed only when she returns to Haiti—to the women who first reared her. What ensues is a passionate journey through a landscape charged with the supernatural and scarred by political violence. In her stunning literary debut, Danticat evokes the wonder, terror, and heartache of her native Haiti—and the enduring strength of Haiti's women—with vibrant imagery and narrative grace that bear witness to her people's suffering and courage.

"Vibrant, magic . . . Danticat's elegant, intricate tale wraps readers into the haunting life of a young Haitian girl." —*The Boston Globe*

"Danticat's calm clarity of vision takes on the resonance of folk art . . . Extraordinarily successful." —*The New York Times Book Review*

"A novel that rewards the reader again and again with small but exquisite and unforgettable epiphanies." —*Washington Post Book World*

About the Author: **Edwidge Danticat** is the author of numerous books, including *Brother, I'm Dying*, which won the National Book Critics Circle Award and was a National Book Award finalist; *Breath, Eyes, Memory*, an Oprah Book Club selection; *Krik? Krak!*, a National Book Award finalist; *The Dew Breaker*, winner of the inaugural Story Prize; *The Farming of Bones*, which won an American Book Award for fiction in 1999; and *Claire of the Sea Light*. The recipient of a MacArthur Fellowship, she has been published in *The New Yorker*, *The New York Times*, and elsewhere.

February 2015 | Trade Paperback | Fiction | 239 pp | $16.00 | ISBN 9781616955021
Soho Press | sohopress.com

CONVERSATION STARTERS

1. Why do you think the author uses French and Haitian Creole words throughout the text? What does the use of either or both languages suggest about class differences among the characters in the novel?

2. How is the use of the colors yellow, red, and blue significant in the novel? What do you think they mean?

3. In the first section of the book, Sophie is often seen pulling a sheet over her head. Why do you think she does that? How do those moments compare to her mother pulling the sheet over her body after she gives her the "test" for the first time?

4. What does Martine mean by "There are secrets you cannot keep." How does Sophie interpret those words?

5. How would you interpret the story of the woman who "walked around with blood constantly spurting out of her unbroken skin." How does that story relate to the lives of the Caco women?

6. Why does Martine finally return to Haiti after staying away for so long? Do you think it was a good idea for her to go?

7. The Caco women seem to mostly communicate through stories. Why do you think that is? What roles do maxims and proverbs play in the novel?

8. Near the end of the book, Tante Atie says, "Young girls should be allowed to keep their pleasant stories." Do you agree? Should everyone be allowed to keep their pleasant stories, even when surrounded by dark realities? Do the Caco women have any pleasant stories?

9. Joseph is extremely understanding, both as a husband and as a father. Is he over-idealized or is he just the kind of man Sophie needs in her life? Do you think things would have turned out differently for Martine if Marc were more like Joseph?

10. At the end of the novel, Sophie's grandmother asks her, "*Ou libere?* Are you free, my daughter?" She also tells her, "Now you will know how to answer." How do you think Sophie would answer? How would you?

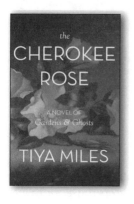

THE CHEROKEE ROSE
A Novel of Gardens and Ghosts
Tiya Miles

Tiya Miles's luminous but highly accessible debut novel examines a little-known aspect of America's past—slaveholding by Southern Creeks and Cherokees—and its legacy in the lives of three young women who are drawn to the Georgia plantation where scenes of extreme cruelty and equally extraordinary compassion once played out.

Set in modern-day Georgia, *The Cherokee Rose* follows three characters—Jinx Micco, a Cherokee-Creek historian exploring her tribe's complicated racial history; Ruth Mayes, whose mother sought refuge from a troubled marriage in her beloved garden and the cosmetic empire she built from its bounty; and Cheyenne Cotterell, an affluent Southern black debutante seeking a meaningful personal history—on their journeys of memory gathering, self-discovery, and bonding. Complementing award-winning research with an ability to write meaningful, complex characters, Miles proves genius again with this debut novel.

"The Cherokee Rose *asks hard questions about race, power, and belonging and reminds us of the fierce love that centers the quest for justice. We need more novels like this.*" —**Daniel Heath Justice, Canada Research Chair in Indigenous Literature and Expressive Culture, University of British Columbia**

"*Poignant and essential storytelling. That only begins to describe Tiya Miles's work.* The Cherokee Rose *is a book that, with a deft hand, illuminates a little-known, yet vitally important, facet of a past we all share. A wonderful read.*" —**Jason Mott, New York Times best-selling author of** *The Returned*

About the Author: **Tiya Miles** was awarded a MacArthur "genius" grant in 2011. She has been selected for *Ebony Magazine's* Power 100 and *The Grio's* 100 lists of African American leaders. The author of numerous works of nonfiction, Miles holds degrees from the University of Minnesota, Emory University, and Harvard University. Currently, she is a professor at the University of Michigan in Ann Arbor, MI.

April 2015 | Hardcover | Fiction | 264 pp | $26.95 | ISBN 9780895876355
John F. Blair, Publisher | blairpub.com | tiyamiles.com

CONVERSATION STARTERS

1. Many Americans can relate to Cheyenne Cotterell's journey to discover her genealogical history. Hearing stories passed down by ancestors is a large part of identity. But what if those stories don't match records such as newspapers, census information, and other documents? Have you ever researched your family tree? Do you have oral histories passed onto you from relatives or ancestors?

2. *The Cherokee Rose* is full of a diverse cast of characters from the past and present. In what ways, big and small, do you see the characters experience or confront prejudice based on their race, class, gender, or sexuality?

3. The plot of *The Cherokee Rose* is really begun when the characters travel to The Cherokee Rose Plantation because it is being auctioned; this is not something that only happens in fiction. Do you feel citizens or governments have a duty to protect historical sites like The Cherokee Rose Plantation? Should there be more done to document and exhibit the true history persevered in such places?

4. *The Cherokee Rose* follows Ruth Mayes and Jinx Micco, both gay women of color, and Cheyenne Cotterell, a black woman trying to discover a lost Native American branch of her family tree. The novel also features historical characters often overlooked in history books and records. In fact, when beginning her research, Tiya Miles was faced with an archivist who laughed at the idea of finding any significant material on African American and Native American women. Do you think *The Cherokee Rose* does well to shine a spotlight on women whose experiences have been all but erased from history? With which character do you most identify? (You can take this Buzzfeed quiz to see which character you're most like!: http://www.buzzfeed.com/annabs/which-kickass-cherokee-rose-character-are-you-13ccj)

5. Tiya Miles's distinguished research delving into the world of a Cherokee-owned slave plantation in present-day Georgia culminated into her works of nonfiction. Her research on that subject and expertise on women's history are the foundations for *The Cherokee Rose*. What aspects of the history presented in the novel surprise you most? Was the author's note about her research enlightening or helpful? Do you think fiction is a good tool to teach people about lesser known people and events of the past?

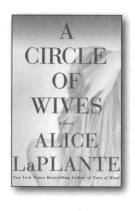

A CIRCLE OF WIVES
Alice LaPlante

An Indie Next Pick, an Amazon Best Book of the Month, a Daily Candy Best Book of the Month, and one of *More* Magazine's "Five Thrillers Not to Read After Dark"

From the bestselling author of *Turn of Mind*, this riveting, complex psychological thriller dissects the intricacies of desire and commitment, trust and jealousy, passion and obsession.

When Dr. John Taylor turns up dead in a hotel room, the local police uncover enough incriminating evidence to suspect foul play. Detective Samantha Adams, whose Palo Alto beat usually covers petty crimes in the wealthy town, is innocently thrown into a high-profile murder case that is more complicated than any she has faced before. A renowned reconstructive surgeon and a respected family man, Dr. Taylor was beloved and admired. But beneath his perfect façade was a hidden life—in fact, multiple lives. Dr. Taylor was married to three very different women in three separate cities. As the curious circumstances surrounding his relationships emerge, Detective Adams finds herself tracking down a murderer through a tangled web of marital deception and revenge.

"Marriage is as mysterious as murder in LaPlante's captivating psychological thriller. . . . A smart, intricate tale about murder and the elusive mysteries of marriage." —**People**

"A suspenseful, thrilling read but also one that explores the complications of human relationships with grace and understanding." —**Interview**

"Love is a mystery in this clever whodunit about marriage, passion and deception. . . . Sharply written and observant." —**Family Circle**

ABOUT THE AUTHOR: **Alice LaPlante** is an award-winning and best-selling author of numerous books, including *Coming of Age at the End of Days* (Available in hardcover August 2015), *A Circle of Wives*, and the *New York Times* bestseller *Turn of Mind*, which was a B&N Discover Award finalist and the winner of the Wellcome Trust's Book Prize.

January 2015 | Trade Paperback | Fiction | 328 pp | $15.00 | ISBN 9780802122926
Grove Press | groveatlantic.com | alicelaplante.com

CONVERSATION STARTERS

1. The book is narrated by four different characters: Detective Samantha Adams and Dr. Taylor's three wives: Helen, MJ, and Deborah. How does this structure provide a more well-rounded understanding of each character? Which of these characters voices do you connect with most? Why?

2. Detective Adams interviews MJ, Helen, and Deborah in back-to-back chapters. What are the similarities and differences in how each wife responds to learning that her husband was married to two other women? What clues are revealed about each wife's potential guilt or innocence in their interviews?

3. Deborah believes that John's three wives "added up to the perfect marriage, and he needed all of us in order to have a balanced life." Does she really mean this? Discuss whether or not Deborah is a reliable narrator.

4. Samantha confronts MJ with the news that MJ had a strong motive to murder Dr. Taylor, as she would have lost her house. "I see now," Samantha says, "that any warmth I felt toward MJ was just stupid me wanting to be liked. We are opponents, have been from the start." Why does this news shock Samantha? Has Samantha's need to be liked impacted her ability to do her job effectively?

5. Helen offers Deborah a place to stay in her apartment, then opens up to Deborah about how she met Dr. Taylor. Are these gestures in line with Helen's character, or do they reflect a genuine reevaluation of her personality in the wake of her pregnancy and Dr. Taylor's death?

6. Why does Deborah indulge Samantha's reenactment of Dr. Taylor's final moments? Is she paying off a debt she feels she owes Samantha? What is Deborah's *quid pro quo* in this scene?

7. Consider whether or not Samantha becomes part of Dr. Taylor's circle of wives. Why or why not?

8. The "Rashomon effect" occurs when multiple speakers narrate a similar event in a contradictory way. How does the structure of A *Circle of Wives* affect our understanding of Dr. Taylor's character? Knowing the outcome of the novel, discuss who was the most reliable and the least reliable narrator.

CLOSE YOUR EYES, HOLD HANDS
Chris Bohjalian

A *Washington Post, St. Louis Post-Dispatch,* and *Milwaukee Journal Sentinel* Best Book of the Year

In a voice that shifts from anguished to sarcastic, heartbroken to hopeful, sixteen-year-old Emily Shepard recounts her solitary odyssey after the meltdown of a nuclear power plant near her home in northern Vermont. Both her parents worked at the plant: her father as chief engineer, her mother as head of public relations. Her father had a reputation as a heavy drinker, and in the media furor that follows the accident he becomes the scapegoat. Evacuated to Burlington with her classmates, Emily realizes her very name puts her in jeopardy. She assumes a new identity as Abby Bliss—the name of the best friend of her idol, the poet Emily Dickinson—and enters the tumultuous world of life on the streets. She briefly finds haven at a shelter for runaways, then moves on to a seedy apartment where she and other teens are forced into drug dealing and prostitution. Escaping to the streets, Emily meets a nine-year-old boy who has run away from an abusive foster home. They form an intense and caring bond until another crisis tears them apart. Alone again, Emily makes one final risky choice, hoping to make peace with her past at last.

The Washington Post called Emily "the most memorable teenage protagonist in recent fiction." As you journey with her, you will be captivated, appalled, and deeply moved by her extraordinary tale.

"*A compelling tale of loss, resilience, and transformation.*" —**The Boston Globe,** "**Pick of the Week**"

"*Chris Bohjalian is a master . . . Emily Shepard is his greatest accomplishment.*" —**Los Angeles Times**

ABOUT THE AUTHOR: **Chris Bohjalian** is the author of seventeen books, including the *New York Times* bestsellers *The Light in the Ruins, The Sandcastle Girls, Skeletons at the Feast,* and *The Double Bind.* His novel *Midwives* was a number one *New York Times* bestseller and a selection of Oprah's Book Club. Three of his books have been made into movies. Bohjalian lives in Vermont with his wife and daughter.

May 2015 | Trade Paperback | Fiction | 288 pp | $15.95 | ISBN 9780307743930
Vintage | penguinrandomhouse.com | chrisbohjalian.com

CONVERSATION STARTERS

1. Emily says, "Obviously I made some bad choices. I'm still here, however, so I made some okay ones, too" (p. 41). How much does her fate depend on her own decisions, wise or unwise? What role do events beyond her control—in particular, the public's unrelenting hostility toward her father—play in these decisions (pp. 41, 53)?

2. In telling her story, Emily moves back and forth in time. How does her narrative reveal her state of mind and the ways in which she perceives or filters her experiences? Do the language and the style accurately reflect the voice of a teenage girl? What passages ring particularly true to you? What is the significance of her noting, "Sometimes when I reread what I've written, I find myself creeped out by what's between the lines. What I haven't written" (p.48)?

3. Why does Emily divide her story into B.C., "Before Cameron," and A.C., "After Cameron"? Does the division represent something more than mere chronology?

4. How would you characterize Emily's decision to return to the Northeast Kingdom? Is she acting foolishly or is her decision understandable, a necessary, essential conclusion to all that has gone before?

5. Many of the stories we read about teens in crisis explore the lives of those raised in crime-ridden, poverty-stricken areas. Emily comes from an educated, upper-middle-class family, and lives in a "meadow mansion." What does she share with troubled teens from less fortunate backgrounds? In what instances do Emily's reactions to her circumstances embody the positive aspects of her upbringing?

6. How would you describe the overall mood and tone of the novel? How does Bohjalian balance the darkness at the heart of the story with an engaging, often humorous portrait of its protagonist? Would you call Emily a heroine? Why or why not?

7. *Close Your Eyes, Hold Hands* deals with some of the most difficult issues of our times: the possibility of nuclear catastrophe, homelessness, drug dealing, prostitution, and child abuse. In what ways does it offer insights that news reports and official studies cannot duplicate?

COAL RIVER
Ellen Marie Wiseman

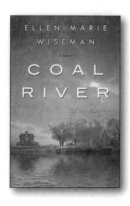

In this vibrant new historical novel, the acclaimed author of *The Plum Tree* and *What She Left Behind* explores one young woman's determination to put an end to child labor in a Pennsylvania mining town...

As a child, Emma Malloy left isolated Coal River, Pennsylvania, vowing never to return. Now, orphaned and penniless at nineteen, she accepts a train ticket from her aunt and uncle and travels back to the rough-hewn community. Treated like a servant by her relatives, Emma works for free in the company store. There, miners and their impoverished families must pay inflated prices for food, clothing, and tools, while those who owe money are turned away to starve.

Most heartrending of all are the breaker boys Emma sees around the village—young children who toil all day sorting coal amid treacherous machinery. Their soot-stained faces remind Emma of the little brother she lost long ago, and she begins leaving stolen food on families' doorsteps, and marking the miners' bills as paid.

Though Emma's actions draw ire from the mine owner and police captain, they lead to an alliance with a charismatic miner who offers to help her expose the truth. And as the lines blur between what is legal and what is just, Emma must risk everything to follow her conscience.

An emotional, compelling novel that rings with authenticity—*Coal River* is a deft and honest portrait of resilience in the face of hardship, and of the simple acts of courage that can change everything.

"*Exquisite.*"— **NY Journal of Books** on **The Plum Tree**

"*A real page turner.*"—**Historical Novel Society** on **What She Left Behind**

ABOUT THE AUTHOR: **Ellen Marie Wiseman** was born and raised in Three Mile Bay, a tiny hamlet in Northern New York. Ellen lives on the shores of Lake Ontario with her husband, two spoiled Shih-Tzus, and a rescued yellow lab. She loves to cook, travel, garden, watch movies, and spend time with her children and grandchildren. For more visit: ellenmariewiseman.com.

December 2015 | Trade Paperback | Fiction | 304 pp | $15.00 | ISBN 9781617734472
Kensington | kensingtonbooks.com | ellenmariewiseman.com

CONVERSATION STARTERS

1. Had you ever heard of the breaker boys before reading *Coal River*? Were you surprised to learn that young boys were used in coal mining?

2. Orphaned and penniless, Emma is forced to choose between the poorhouse and going back to Coal River where her brother drowned and her uncle mistreated her. Considering the times, what do you think would have happened to Emma if she had chosen the poorhouse? What would you have done?

3. How do you think Emma changed over the course of the novel? What were the most important events that facilitated those changes? Why do you think she was so determined to help the breaker boys?

4. How did you feel about Clayton when you first met him? Did you trust him? What about Nally? How were Clayton and Nally the same? How were they different?

5. Emma is doubtful that her dead brother is speaking to her through Michael. In the end she is still not sure. What do you think? Do you believe in channeling and mediums?

6. How did you feel about Percy when you first met him? How about Frank? Did you end up feeling differently about them by the end of the book? Why?

7. What do you think Frank's motives were when he told Hazard Flint that Emma was becoming friendly with the miners' wives and children? Why did it backfire?

8. Twice, Emma risked her life to save Frank. Why do you think she did it? Would you risk your life to save someone who had harmed or mistreated you?

9. Even though Pennsylvania child labor laws came into effect in the late 1800s, many mine owners got away with putting underage boys to work in the breaker and mine until the 1920s. Why do you think it was allowed to continue for so long? What could have been done to stop it?

10. At the end of Coal River, secrets were revealed that changed everything. Which ones surprised you the most? Did you see any of them coming?

....

THE DAUGHTERS
Adrienne Celt

In this virtuoso debut, a world-class soprano seeks to reclaim her voice from the curse that winds through her family tree.

Since the difficult birth of her daughter, renowned opera sensation Lulu can't bring herself to sing a note. Haunted by a curse that traces back through the women in her family, she fears that the loss of her remarkable talent and the birth of her daughter are somehow inextricably connected. As Lulu tentatively embraces motherhood, she sifts through the stories she's inherited about her elusive, jazz-singing mother and the nearly mythic matriarch, her great-grandmother Greta. Each tale is steeped in the family's folkloric Polish tradition and haunted by the *rusulka*—a spirit that inspired Dvorak's classic opera.

Merging elements from *Bel Canto* and *Amy and Isabelle*, *The Daughters* reveals through four generations the sensuous but precise physicality of both music and motherhood, and—most mysterious and seductive of all—the resonant ancestral lore that binds each mother to the one who came before.

"A haunting novel with real emotional depth, Celt's psychologically nuanced debut continues to resonate long after the last page has been turned."— **Kirkus Reviews, starred review**

"[A] modern fairy tale that had me up from my chair in standing ovation." — **Sarah McCoy, New York Times and international best-selling author of The Mapmaker's Children**

"[A] resonant meditation on the way our stories at once shape and sabotage our lives."—**Publishers Weekly**

"A beautifully written exploration of the myths and the realities that bind families together that will leave readers eagerly awaiting Celt's next novel." —**Booklist**

About the Author: **Adrienne Celt**'s work has been published in *Esquire*, the Kenyon Review, the *Rumpus*, and elsewhere, and she holds an MFA from Arizona State University. She lives in Tucson, and she has a Polish grandmother of her own.

August 2015 | Hardcover | Fiction | 272 pp | $24.95 | ISBN 9781631490453
Liveright | wwnorton.com

CONVERSATION STARTERS

1. Before giving birth, Lulu often describes her body as "tightly wound," but after having Kara her body is loosened, expansive, "cracked open." What does this seem to suggest of Lulu's experience of motherhood?

2. Why do you think Sara leaves Ada and Lulu behind? What effect does her absence have on Lulu?

3. Do you think John suspects Kara is not his own daughter? If so, why do you think he chooses not to confront Lulu?

4. Lulu believes the function of stories is to "teach our brains to dream." What do you think is the purpose of storytelling in this narrative?

5. Lulu seems deeply aware of her sensory surroundings, and is particularly sensitive to touch and sound. Her spine "cracks" as she shifts in her chair, sound "breaks into brittle sheets of paper," a voice is "spongelike;" what do you think this reveals of her character?

6. When Lulu says of John that he "makes the world what he wants it to be," what do you think she means? How would you describe John?

7. Often the stories told in the novel—from Ada's rich folktales and Sara's playful games to Lulu's childhood fantasies—take an unexpected turn. Why do you think that is?

8. How does Ada handle her grief over losing Greta, and the loss of her home in the wake of war? How does her grief compare to Lulu's?

9. What do you make of the differences in Greta's story when Ada and Sara tell it?

10. Why does John's rabbit story hold such significance for Lulu? What does it seem to tell her about him, about their relationship?

11. Which character do you sympathize with most in the story?

12. How did you feel about the ending? Do you feel hopeful for Lulu and her relationship with Sara? Her relationship with Kara?

ELIZABETH IS MISSING
Emma Healey

Maud is forgetful. She makes a cup of tea and doesn't remember to drink it. She goes to the shops and forgets why she went. Sometimes her home is unrecognizable—or her daughter, Helen, seems a total stranger.

But there's one thing Maud is sure of: her friend Elizabeth is missing. The note in her pocket tells her so. And no matter who tells her to stop going on about it, to leave it alone, to shut up, Maud will get to the bottom of it.

Because somewhere in Maud's damaged mind lies the answer to an unsolved seventy-year-old mystery. One everyone has forgotten about.

Everyone, except Maud . . .

A page-turning story of suspense, *Elizabeth Is Missing* hauntingly reminds us that we are all at the mercy of our memory. Always compelling, often poignant, and at times even blackly witty, this is an absolutely unforgettable novel.

"[A] spellbinding first novel." —**New York Times Book Review**

"[A] knockout debut. . . . Ms. Healey's audacious conception and formidable talent combine in a bravura performance that sustains its momentum and pathos to the last." —**Wall Street Journal**

"Elizabeth is Missing *will stir and shake you."* —**Emma Donoghue**

"Very good indeed." —**Jojo Moyes, author of** *Me Before You*

"Ingeniously structured and remarkably poignant, Elizabeth is Missing *is a riveting story of friendship and loss that will have you compulsively puzzling fact from fiction as you race to the last page."* —**Kimberly McCreight, New York Times bestselling author of** *Reconstructing Amelia*

ABOUT THE AUTHOR: **Emma Healey** holds a degree in bookbinding and an MA in creative writing. *Elizabeth Is Missing* is her first novel. She lives in the United Kingdom.

June 2015 | Trade Paperback | Fiction | 320 pp | $15.99 | ISBN 9780062309686
Harper Perennial | harpercollins.com | emmahealey.co.uk

CONVERSATION STARTERS

1. What interesting and complex narrative effects result from the narrator having such difficulty with her memory?

2. How does the consistent shift from present to past affect the telling of the story? How does the author transition between them?

3. In Chapter 1 there are several allusions to Little Red Riding Hood. In what ways might this fairy tale be relevant to the story?

4. Carla, one of Maud's caregivers, often tells of horrible crimes she's read about in the news. What does this add to the novel? How does it affect Maud?

5. What is the difference between something or someone being missing, lost, or gone? Consider various points of view.

6. In what relevant ways does the war—and all the lengthy separations it causes—affect the people and relationships in the novel?

7. What is the importance and effect of "the mad woman" throughout the novel?

8. Both Douglas and Frank seemingly have moments of menace and kindness. Compare and contrast them.

9. In Chapter 10, Maud, having forgotten what room she was headed to, says, "I must be going mad." Compare and contrast her with "the mad woman."

10. What does the subject of Maud's childhood illness add to the story?

11. Throughout her life, but especially once her sister Sukey goes missing, Maud collects random, found objects. How do physical objects come to possess meaning or value?

12. At one point, speaking to Frank, Maud denies she has secrets, but then admits to liking the idea. How might secrets be important? How can they be unhealthy?

13. Late in the novel, Maud touches something of her sister's and says, "The contact makes it possible to breathe again." What is she experiencing?

14. Consider the Epilogue. What is the effect of ending the novel with the lyric swirl of Maud's receding memories?

EUPHORIA
Lily King

New York Times Bestseller
Winner of the New England Book Award for Fiction
Winner of the Kirkus Prize
A Finalist for the National Book Critics Circle Award

A Best Book of the Year for:

New York Times Book Review, Time, NPR, Washington Post, Entertainment Weekly, Newsday, Vogue, New York Magazine, Seattle Times, San Francisco Chronicle, Wall Street Journal, Boston Globe, The Guardian, Kirkus Reviews, Amazon, Publishers Weekly, **Our Man in Boston, Oprah.com, Salon**

Euphoria is Lily King's nationally bestselling breakout novel of three young, gifted anthropologists of the '30's caught in a passionate love triangle that threatens their bonds, their careers, and, ultimately, their lives. Inspired by events in the life of revolutionary anthropologist Margaret Mead, Euphoria is "dazzling ... suspenseful ... brilliant...an exhilarating novel."
—*Boston Globe*

"A meticulously researched homage to [Margaret] Mead's restless mind... taut, witty, fiercely intelligent ... The steam the book emits is as much intellectual as erotic."—**New York Times Book Review** (cover review)

"Enthralling . . . From Conrad to Kingsolver, the misdeeds of Westerners have inspired their own literary subgenre, and in King's insightful, romantic addition, the work of novelist and anthropologist find resonant parallel."
—*Vogue*

"You need know not one thing about 1930s cultural anthropology, or about the late, controversial anthropologists Margaret Mead and Reo Fortune and Gregory Bateson... to delight in King's novel."—*San Francisco Chronicle*

ABOUT THE AUTHOR: **Lily King** is the author of *The Pleasing Hour, The English Teacher,* and *Father of the Rain.* She is winner of the Kirkus Prize, two time winner of the New England Book Award for Fiction and a NYTBR Top Ten Book of the year author. She lives with her family in Maine.

April 2015 | Trade Paperback | Fiction | 288 pp | $16.00 | ISBN 9780802123701
Grove Press | groveatlantic.com | lilykingbooks.com

CONVERSATION STARTERS

1. Set against the lush tropical landscape of 1930s New Guinea, this novel charts British anthropologist Andrew Bankson's fascination for colleagues Nell Stone and her husband, Fen, a fascination that turns deadly. How far does the setting play a role in shaping events? Is there a sense that the three have created their own small universe on the banks of the Sepik River, far removed from the Western world? If so, by whose rules are they playing?

2. Over the course of the novel we learn a great deal about Bankson's childhood and young adulthood. Talk about the reasons and life events that brought him to anthropology. What has led him to the brink of suicide? How seriously do you think he views his statement: "The meaning of life is the quest to understand the structure and order of the natural world—that was the mantra I was raised on. To deviate from it was suicide" (p. 32).

3. How far would you consider Nell to be the epitome of a young, independent accomplished woman? Talk about her character, her personality, work habits and motivations. Then discuss her disturbing relationship with Fen, and her inability to escape his harm. How did she end up in such an untenable situation?

4. What do the three of them really see in the tribes of New Guinea? To what extent, when unlocking the puzzles of the Kiona and the Tam, are they searching for meaning within themselves? How important is it to impending events that the Tam tribe appears to be female-dominated?

5. For all of Nell and Bankson's heartfelt conversations, and Bankson's keen observations of her at work, there are many important things left unsaid. Nell states: "You don't realize how language actually interferes with communication … how it gets in the way like an overdominant sense" (p. 79). Should Bankson have understood further Nell's sadness within her marriage, Fen's physical abuse? As a reader, do we miss the clues too?

EVERYTHING I NEVER TOLD YOU
Celeste Ng

New York Times Bestseller, A *New York Times Book Review* Editor's Choice, Best Book of the Year: NPR, *San Francisco Chronicle*, *Entertainment Weekly*, *The Huffington Post*, *Buzzfeed*, *Book Riot*, *School Library Journal*

"Lydia is dead. But they don't know this yet." So begins this exquisite novel about a Chinese American family living in 1970s small-town Ohio. Lydia is the favorite child of Marilyn and James Lee, and her parents are determined that she will fulfill the dreams they were unable to pursue. But when Lydia's body is found in the local lake, the delicate balancing act that has been keeping the Lee family together is destroyed, tumbling them into chaos. A profoundly moving story of family, secrets, and longing, *Everything I Never Told You* is both a gripping page-turner and a sensitive family portrait, uncovering the ways in which mothers and daughters, fathers and sons, and husbands and wives struggle, all their lives, to understand one another.

"If we know this story, we haven't seen it yet in American fiction, not until now . . . Ng has set two tasks in this novel's doubled heart—to be exciting, and to tell a story bigger than whatever is behind the crime. She does both by turning the nest of familial resentments into at least four smaller, prickly mysteries full of secrets the family members won't share… What emerges is a deep, heartfelt portrait of a family struggling with its place in history, and a young woman hoping to be the fulfillment of that struggle. This is, in the end, a novel about the burden of being the first of your kind—a burden you do not always survive." —**Alexander Chee, *The New York Times Book Review***

"Excellent…an accomplished debut . . . heart-wrenching…Ng deftly pulls together the strands of this complex, multigenerational novel. Everything I Never Told You *is an engaging work that casts a powerful light on the secrets that have kept an American family together—and that finally end up tearing it apart."* —**Los Angeles Times**

ABOUT THE AUTHOR: **Celeste Ng** grew up in Pittsburgh, Pennsylvania, and Shaker Heights, Ohio. She attended Harvard University and earned an MFA from the University of Michigan. She lives in Cambridge, Massachusetts, with her husband and son.

May 2015 | Trade Paperback | Fiction | 320 pp | $16.00 | ISBN 9780143127550
Penguin Books | penguinrandomhouse.com | celesteng.com

CONVERSATION STARTERS

1. Discuss the relationships between Nath, Lydia, and Hannah. How do the siblings both understand and mystify one another?

2. Why do you think Lydia is the favorite child of James and Marilyn? How does this pressure affect Lydia, and what kind of impact do you think it has on Nath and Hannah? Do you think it is more difficult for Lydia to be the favorite, or for Nath and Hannah, who are often overlooked by their parents?

3. How did you react to the "Marco Polo" pool scene with James and Nath? What do you think of James's decision?

4. How do the members of the Lee family deal with being measured against stereotypes and others' perceptions?

5. What is the meaning of the novel's title? To whom do the "I" and "You" refer?

6. What would have happened if Lydia had reached the dock? Do you think she would have been able to change her parents' views and expectations of her?

7. This novel says a great deal about the influence parents can have. Do you think the same issues will affect the next generation of Lees?

8. "It struck her then, as if someone had said it aloud: her mother was dead, and the only thing worth remembering about her, in the end, was that she cooked. Marilyn thought uneasily of her own life, of hours spent making breakfasts, serving dinners, packing lunches into neat paper bags." Discuss the relationship Marilyn and her mother have to cooking and their roles as stay-at-home mothers. Do you think one is happier or more satisfied?

9. The footprint on the ceiling brings Nath and Lydia closer when they are young, and later, Hannah and James discover it together and laugh. What other objects bring the characters closer together or drive them further apart?

10. There's so much that the characters keep to themselves. What do you wish they had shared with one another? Do you think an ability to better express themselves would have changed the outcome of the book?

FOR TODAY I AM A BOY
Kim Fu

A *New York Times Book Review* Editor's Choice

2015 PEN/Hemingway Award, Finalist

A fiercely assured debut novel about four second-generation Chinese sisters, one of whom happens to be a boy.

At birth, Peter Huang is given the Chinese name Juan Chaun, "powerful king." To his parents, newly settled in small-town Ontario, he is the exalted only son in a sea of daughters, the one who will finally fulfill his immigrant father's dreams of Western masculinity. Peter and his sisters grow up in an airless house of order and obligation, though secrets and half-truths simmer beneath the surface. At the first opportunity, each of the girls lights out on her own. But for Peter, escape is not as simple as fleeing his parents' home. Though his father crowned him "powerful king," Peter knows otherwise. He knows he is really a girl. With the help of his far-flung sisters and the sympathetic souls he finds along the way, Peter inches ever closer to his own life, his own skin, in this darkly funny, emotionally acute, stunningly powerful debut.

*"[A] sharply written debut . . . A coming-of-age tale for our time." —**Seattle Times***

*"Sensitively wrought . . . For Today I Am a Boy is as much about the construction of self as the consequences of its unwitting destruction—and what happens when its acceptance seems as foreign as another country." —**New York Times Book Review***

*"Subtle and controlled, with flashes of humor and warmth." —**Slate***

*"Keeps you reading. Told in snatches of memory that hurt so much they have the ring of truth." —**Bust magazine***

ABOUT THE AUTHOR: **Kim Fu** was born in 1987 and holds a master of fine arts degree from the University of British Columbia. She lives in Seattle.

March 2015 | Trade Paperback | Fiction | 256 pp | $14.95 | ISBN 9780544538528
Houghton Mifflin Harcourt | hmhco.com | kimfu.ca

CONVERSATION STARTERS

1. Kim Fu quotes from the song "For Today I Am a Boy" by Antony and the Johnsons: "One day I'll grow up, I'll be a beautiful woman. One day I'll grow up, I'll be a beautiful girl. But for today, I am a child. For today, I am a boy." What questions does this quotation evoke? Does the reference lend nuances to the title?

2. Peter grows up associating with boys like Roger and Ollie, who are rough, physical, and crude. In one powerful incident Peter is pushed by Roger and Ollie to attack a young girl. When Peter returns home, his mother slaps him, yet his father smiles and tells him he will have his own room. How does Peter handle these mixed messages?

3. There's not much interaction between Peter and his father, yet when interaction does occur, it provides powerful messages about men and women. Consider when Peter's father says, "Women bleed more," or when he refers to "women's work." What do these moments create for Peter?

4. Chef shares the story of how he had sex with a man he thought was a woman. Peter fixates on the conversation between Chef and Simon. With whose perspective about this episode do you agree? Do you think it's wrong of people to deceive others about such matters? Why?

5. After finding some friends who seem to understand and support his situation, Peter begins to experience life as a woman. He dances with a man during a Halloween party, yet part of him will not let go of his plight: "It's Halloween, it's just a game, it isn't real." What is it that Peter needs to feel secure?

6. Eileen provides the final catalyst for Peter. "You don't have to look like that to be a woman. That's not what being a woman means" (237). Do you agree with her? What does it mean to be a woman? How has society defined what it means to be a woman?

7. Peter says that he "could not pin down what would be enough, other than resetting time, going back before my birth, before my conception, and finding a way to choose" (115). Has Peter found peace and acceptance?

THE GARDEN OF EVENING MISTS
Tan Twan Eng

Malaya, 1951. Yun Ling Teoh, the scarred lone survivor of a brutal Japanese wartime camp, seeks solace among the jungle-fringed tea plantations of Cameron Highlands. There she discovers Yugiri, the only Japanese garden in Malaya, and its owner and creator, the enigmatic Aritomo, exiled former gardener of the emperor of Japan. Despite her hatred of the Japanese, Yun Ling seeks to engage Aritomo to create a garden in memory of her sister, who died in the camp. Aritomo refuses but agrees to accept Yun Ling as his apprentice "until the monsoon comes." Then she can design a garden for herself.

As the months pass, Yun Ling finds herself intimately drawn to the gardener and his art, while all around them a communist guerilla war rages. But the Garden of Evening Mists remains a place of mystery. Who is Aritomo and how did he come to leave Japan? And is the real story of how Yun Ling managed to survive the war perhaps the darkest secret of all?

"A strong quiet novel of eloquent mystery." —**The New York Times Book Review**

"Grace and empathy infuse this melancholy landscape of complex loyalties enfolded by brutal history, creating a novel of peculiar, mysterious, tragic beauty." —**The Kirkus Review, STARRED REVIEW**

"Like his debut, The Gift of Rain (2007), Tan's second novel is exquisite... Tan triumphs again." —**Library Journal, STARRED REVIEW**

"Beautifully written...Eng is quite simply one of the best novelists writing today." —**Philadelphia Inquirer**

ABOUT THE AUTHOR: **Tan Twan Eng** was born in Penang, Malaysia. He divides his time between Kuala Lumpur and Cape Town. *The Gift of Rain*, his first novel, was Longlisted for the Man Booker Prize. His second and latest novel, *The Garden of Evening Mists*, was Shortlisted for the Man Booker Prize 2012 and won the Man Asian Literary Prize (March 2013), and the Walter Scott Prize (2013).

September 2012 | Trade Paperback | Fiction | 352 pp | $15.99 | ISBN 9781602861800
Weinstein Books | weinsteinbooks.com | tantwaneng.com

CONVERSATION STARTERS

1. The author introduces Yun Ling as she is entering retirement, and slowly reveals the key experiences that have shaped her life. What was your initial impression of the main character and how did it change as the novel progressed?

2. As a research clerk in the war crimes tribunal directly after the war, Yun Ling is intimately involved in the national process of punishment and healing after the horrors of the Japanese invasion. Yet, she is hardly healed, and she has her own motives for this work. Can the Japanese crimes be forgiven?

3. Violence is a frequent presence in Yun Ling's life, from the labor camp to the CT invasion to the destruction of her memory. How does she cope with the trauma of these events? Is she successful?

4. Not just violence, but sexual violence is a factor in the novel. How did you grapple with Yun Hong's experience as one of the "comfort women" in the camp and the shame she felt as a result?

5. Intertwined with the traumatic episodes, art – including literature, painting, and, of course, garden design – appears constantly in the book. Consider some key examples (i.e., Yun Hong's painting, the supposed Golden Lily hoard, Yugiri itself) and discuss their importance to the novel.

6. Aritomo's final artistic work is not a garden but a horimono, a tattoo covering much of Yun Ling's battered body. What is the significance of this act to their relationship and to the novel?

7. There is a constant struggle between memory and forgetting in the novel. How does the experience of the camp change Yun Ling's relationship to memory?

8. Frederik and Yun Ling have a brief encounter when she first arrives at Majuba estate, and he makes it clear that he has strong feelings for her throughout the book. Why do you think Yun Ling chooses Aritomo over Frederik?

9. Why does Yun Ling, after all her searching and striving, choose not to use the possible clues from her horimono to try and locate her camp? Is this a hopeful novel?

THE GIRL FROM THE TRAIN
Irma Joubert

Set during the harrowing, final moments of World War II, Polish resistance fighter Jakób Kowalski is planting a bomb on the tracks intending to destroy a German troop transport, but six-year-old Gretl Schmidt's unscheduled train bound for Auschwitz reaches the bomb first. Gretl is the only survivor. Though spared from the concentration camp, the orphaned German Jew finds herself now lost in a hostile country. When Jakób discovers her, guilt and compassion prompt him to hide and protect Gretl in his home concealed from his Catholic family. For years, the young man and little girl form a bond over the secrets they must hide from the world. But she can't stay with him forever. Jakób makes the difficult choice to send Gretl to South Africa, where German war orphans are promised bright futures with adoptive Protestant families—so long as Gretl's Jewish roots, Catholic education, and connections to communist Poland are never discovered. Separated by continents, politics, religion, language, and years, Jakób and Gretl will likely never see each other again. But the events they have both survived and their belief in the human spirit forge an unbreakable bond of love.

"Readers will adore intrepid Gretl and strong Jakób in this story of war, redemption, and love." —**Publishers Weekly**

"Joubert masterfully crafts every scene with tenderness and hauntingly accurate detail. It's a stunning coming-of-age novel that packs emotion in a delicate weave of hope, faith—and the very best of love."
—**Kristy Cambron, author of** *The Butterfly and the Violin*

About the Author: **Irma Joubert**, international bestselling author, was a history teacher for 35 years before she began writing. Her stories are known for their deep insight into personal relationships and rich historical detail. She's the author of eight novels and a regular fixture on bestseller lists in The Netherlands and in her native South Africa. Connect with Irma at GirlFromTheTrain.com.

November 2015 | Trade Paperback | Fiction | 384 pp | $15.99 | ISBN 9780529102379
Thomas Nelson | harpercollins.com

CONVERSATION STARTERS

1. How does Gretl experience a conflicted identity when we meet her in the opening chapters of the novel, and how does this conflict of identity resolve throughout the course of the story?

2. How does Jakób's own journey mirror Gretl's, and in what way are their journeys different?

3. What did you learn about the political situation in WWII and post-WWII Poland that you didn't know before reading this book?

4. What did you learn about the political situation in WWII and post-WWII South Africa that you didn't know before reading this book?

5. Discuss the role of Grandpa John in the story. How does he serve as a bridge for Gretl between her past history and her present life? Why is their relationship unique and special?

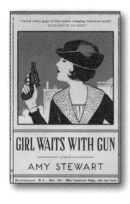

GIRL WAITS WITH GUN
Amy Stewart

From the *New York Times* best-selling author of *The Drunken Botanist* comes an enthralling novel based on the forgotten true story of one of the nation's first female crime fighters.

Constance Kopp doesn't quite fit the mold. She towers over most men, has no interest in marriage or domestic affairs, and has been isolated from the world since a family secret sent her and her sisters from city to country fifteen years ago. When a powerful, ruthless factory owner runs down their buggy, a dispute over damages turns into a war of bricks, bullets, and threats as he unleashes his gang on their farm. The sheriff enlists her help, and it turns out Constance has knack for outwitting (and disarming) the criminal element that might just take her back out into the world and onto a new path in life. Quick-witted and full of madcap escapades, *Girl Waits with Gun* is a story about one woman rallying the courage to stand up for and grow into herself — with a little help from sisters and sheriffs along the way.

Through Amy Stewart's exuberant storytelling, Constance Kopp catapults from forgotten historical anecdote to unforgettable historical fiction heroine — an outsized woman not only ahead of her time but sometimes, even, ahead of ours.

"A smart, romping adventure, featuring some of the most memorable and powerful female characters I've seen in print for a long time. I loved every page as I followed the Kopp sisters through a too-good-to-be-true (but mostly true!) tale of violence, courage, stubbornness, and resourcefulness."
— **Elizabeth Gilbert, *New York Times* best-selling author of *The Signature of All Things***

ABOUT THE AUTHOR: **Amy Stewart** is the award-winning author of six books, including the bestsellers *The Drunken Botanist* and *Wicked Plants*. She and her husband live in Eureka, California, where they own a bookstore called Eureka Books.

September 2015 | Hardcover | Fiction | 416 pp | $27.00 | ISBN 9780544409910
Houghton Mifflin Harcourt | hmhco.com | amystewart.com

CONVERSATION STARTERS

1. From horse-drawn wagons to carrier pigeons, the norms of 1914 obviously no longer exist today. Talk about the world Constance and her sisters live in, in New Jersey and on their farm. Are there any aspects of life in 1914 you wish had survived?

2. After Henry Kaufman's first visit to their farm, Constance views her sisters from afar and thinks, "They looked like those fuzzy figures in a picture postcard, frozen in place, staring out from some world that no longer existed" (p. 52). What is the world that no longer exists? Why is it gone, and what has replaced it?

3. What is it about Lucy Blake's story that haunts Constance so? Why do you think she helps her when interfering with Henry Kaufman has already brought a threat to her family?

4. It's clear that Constance is a unique woman for her time. But Sheriff Heath is also unusual in that he takes the Kopp sisters seriously when no one else would. Why do you think he helps them? What would you have done in their shoes?

5. At their Wyckoff farm, both Norma and Constance were encouraged to continue their mother's "family tradition" of fear and distrust. In what ways did the sisters fall in line, and in what ways did they fail to heed her warnings? Do you think they felt justified in ignoring her warnings?

6. On page 384, Fleurette suggests that their year of harassment at the hands of Henry Kaufman was also the most interesting year of their lives, and therefore might not have been such a bad thing in the end. What if it were you—would you agree with Fleurette?

7. The author created a signature cocktail for the book called the New Jersey Automobile based on an actual 1910s-era cocktail called the Automobile. What would Norma think about an alcoholic beverage being named after their run-in with Henry Kaufman?

8. There's a lot of talk these days about characters' likability. Would you call the Kopp sisters likable? Do you think they even liked each other?

9. Did you suspect the family secret? When did you figure it out?

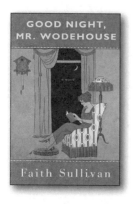

GOOD NIGHT, MR. WODEHOUSE
Faith Sullivan

From the *New York Times* best-selling author of *The Cape Ann* comes a novel of friendship, survival, and the sustaining bonds between a reader and her most beloved author

In *Good Night, Mr. Wodehouse*, Faith Sullivan returns to Harvester, Minnesota—the setting of her bestseller *The Cape Ann*—to tell the story of Nell Stillman, an ordinary woman with an extraordinary life.

Nell's road has not been easy: a complicated marriage; a widowhood spent longing for her congressman lover; the responsibility of caring for her son, a shell-shocked WWI hero. Whether her days bring joy or turmoil, Nell ends each evening by visiting her lifelong literary companions, including Chekhov, Austen, and especially the light-hearted and gentlemanly P.G. Wodehouse.

Spanning the first half of the twentieth century, *Good Night, Mr. Wodehouse* demonstrates the power of great novels to transform and even save our lives.

"Good Night, Mr. Wodehouse is told with Faith Sullivan's trademark warmth, wit and wisdom. Readers, prepare to be captivated." —**Lorna Landvik, author of *Angry Houswives Eating Bon Bons***

"Sullivan's many richly imagined characters walk right out of these pages into our lives. A beautiful and profound novel." —**Margot Livesey, author of *The Flight of Gemma Hardy***

"For all those fans of The Cape Ann, Gardenias, and The Empress of One: here is your priceless ticket back to Harvester, Minnesota, where Lark, Sally and others vividly await. An extraordinary book." —**Julie Schumacher, author of *Dear Committee Members***

ABOUT THE AUTHOR: **Faith Sullivan** is the author of seven award-winning novels including the national bestseller, *The Cape Ann*. Sullivan was born and raised in southern Minnesota and has visited with well over 1,000 book clubs. She lives in Minneapolis with her husband.

September 2015 | Hardcover | Fiction | 456 pp | $26.00 | ISBN 9781571311115
Milkweed Editions | milkweed.org | faithsullivan.org

CONVERSATION STARTERS

1. Harvester is a typical small town, complete with both close-knit bonds and an insidious gossip mill. How do these two characteristics affect one another? As the balance between them shifts with changing circumstances, how does each influence the trajectory of Nell's life?

2. Nell uses P.G. Wodehouse's novels as a means to survive loss and hardship. What about these novels does she find so comforting? What role do these books play in her relationships with others?

3. Nell receives a series of cryptic letters after Elvira leaves town. What effect do these letters have on Nell? Who do you think the sender is, and does his or her specific identity matter?

4. Letters have a powerful influence on the progression of Nell's story. What is the significance of the fact that so often, words on a page are driving forces in her life?

5. Nell's husband Bert begins the narrative by shaming Nell for being a Catholic woman who "enjoys the bedroom." How do diverse faith traditions affect the town's perceptions of and relationships with different characters in the book?

6. Nell ages more than sixty years in *Good Night, Mr. Wodehouse*. What do you think are the most defining moments for her character's growth and evolution?

7. Over time, Nell's concept of and feelings about the institution of marriage become increasingly complicated. Considering the historical context, what does it take for her to live out her convictions?

8. From the opening page, Nell is presented as highly independent. In what ways does this independence express itself differently throughout her life? What outside circumstances enable or support these choices, both large and small?

9. In many ways, this is a novel about different kinds of affection—between parents and children, between friends, between lovers. How do the characters' loyalties to these various relationships shift over time, and what effect does this loyalty have on their own lives?

10. If Nell were alive today, what books would she read for comfort, inspiration, and strength?

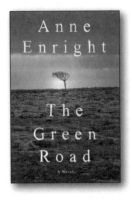

THE GREEN ROAD
Anne Enright

Available now in hardcover and ebook. Coming to paperback in May 2016.

From internationally acclaimed author Anne Enright comes a shattering novel set in a small town on Ireland's Atlantic coast. *The Green Road* is a tale of family and fracture, compassion and selfishness—a book about the gaps in the human heart and how we strive to fill them.

Spanning thirty years, The Green Road tells the story of Rosaleen, matriarch of the Madigans, a family on the cusp of either coming together or falling irreparably apart. As they grow up, Rosaleen's four children leave the west of Ireland for lives they could have never imagined in Dublin, New York, and Mali, West Africa. In her early old age their difficult, wonderful mother announces that she's decided to sell the house and divide the proceeds. Her adult children come back for a last Christmas, with the feeling that their childhoods are being erased, their personal history bought and sold.

A profoundly moving work about a family's desperate attempt to recover the relationships they've lost and forge the ones they never had, *The Green Road* is Enright's most mature, accomplished, and unforgettable novel to date.

"With language so vibrant it practically has a pulse, Enright makes an exquisitely drawn case for the possibility of growth, love and transformation at any age." —***People***

"Enright…is a master of emotional excavation. …Through her wise and majestic book, [she] shows us the beauty even in life's harsh terrain. —*O Magazine*

About the Author: **Anne Enright** was born in Dublin, where she now lives and works. She has published three volumes of stories, one book of nonfiction, and five novels. In 2015, she was named the inaugural Laureate for Irish Fiction. Her novel *The Gathering* won the Man Booker Prize, and her last novel, *The Forgotten Waltz*, won the Andrew Carnegie Medal for Excellence in Fiction.

May 2015 | Hardcover | Fiction | 304 pp | $26.95 | ISBN 9780393248210
May 2016 | Trade Paperback | Fiction | 304 pp | $15.95 | ISBN 9780393352801
W.W. Norton & Company | Subscribe to the newsletter at wwnorton.com/reading-guides

CONVERSATION STARTERS

1. All of the children move out of Rosaleen's orbit and establish their own lives elsewhere. How does their homecoming affect them?

2. Rosaleen writes distinct Christmas cards to each of her children. What does her card to each child tell you about their relationship? What do the cards tell you about her?

3. After Dan announces his decision to become a priest, Rosaleen says, "I made him. I made him the way he is. And I don't like the way he is. He is my son and I don't like him, and he doesn't like me either" (34). What role does dislike play in her relationship with Dan?

4. Enright writes, "Emmet . . . was drawn to suffering—it was, after all, his job" (106). Is his interest in suffering heroic or self-absorbed?

5. Dan, Hanna, Constance, and Emmet all have aspects of their private lives that they do not share with one another. What do they hide from one another, and why?

6. Emmet is described as not having "the helplessness in him that love required" (249). From Dan during the AIDS crisis in New York to Rosaleen on the green road, how are helplessness and love portrayed as related in the novel?

7. Toward the end of the novel, Enright describes Rosaleen on the green road: "there were gaps between things, and this frightened her. This is where Rosaleen was now. She had fallen into the gap" (266). What does this "gap" mean for Rosaleen and her relationship with the green road?

8. Pat Madigan is largely absent throughout the narrative. How does his absence shape the novel?

9. Anne Enright has said that a major theme of *The Green Road* is compassion. How do members of the Madigan family show compassion to one another?

10. Of Rosaleen, Enright writes, "her life was one of great harmlessness" (149). Do you agree?

11. The house in County Clare is the most prominent home in the novel. How have Rosaleen's children chased, established, or resisted establishing their own homes?

H IS FOR HAWK
Helen Macdonald

New York Times Bestseller
Amazon's #1 Best Book of the Year So Far
Winner of the Samuel Johnson Prize
Named the Costa Book of the Year

When Helen Macdonald's father died suddenly on a London street, she was devastated. An experienced falconer—Helen had been captivated by hawks since childhood—she'd never before been tempted to train one of the most vicious predators, the goshawk. But in her grief, she saw that the goshawk's fierce and feral temperament mirrored her own. Resolving to purchase and raise the deadly creature as a means to cope with her loss, she adopted Mabel, and turned to the guidance of *The Once and Future King* author T.H. White's chronicle *The Goshawk* to begin her challenging endeavor. Projecting herself "in the hawk's wild mind to tame her" tested the limits of Macdonald's humanity and changed her life.

"Breathtaking . . . Helen Macdonald renders an indelible impression of a raptor's fierce essence—and her own—with words that mimic feathers, so impossibly pretty we don't notice their astonishing engineering."—**New York Times Book Review** (**cover review**)

"[An] instant classic."—**Dwight Garner, *New York Times***

"Dazzling."—***Vogue***

"[A] singular book that combines memoir and landscape, history and falconry."—**Susan Straight, *Los Angeles Times***

"Extraordinary . . . indelible."—**Lev Grossman, *TIME***

"A meditation on the bond between beasts and humans and the pain and beauty of being alive." —***People*** (**Book of the Week**)

"A superior accomplishment . . . Macdonald has found the ideal balance between art and truth." —***Seattle Times***

About the Author: **Helen Macdonald** is a writer, poet, illustrator, historian, and naturalist who lives in Cambridge, England. She is also the author of the poetry collection *Shaler's Fish*.

March 2015 | Hardcover | Fiction | 320 pp | $25.00 | ISBN 9780802123411
Grove Press | groveatlantic.com

CONVERSATION STARTERS

1. In the book's opening pages, Macdonald writes, "The wild can be human work." (8) Literally, she wrote this sentence to explain how British goshawks were brought back from extinction by falconers who imported birds from the continent which were lost or released and subsequently bred. What other meanings could this line have? What does this tell us about the kind of narrator Helen will be?

2. Macdonald was eight years old when she first reads T.H. White's *The Goshawk*, a book that proves a formative experience. She initially dislikes the book. "Why would a grown up write about *not* being able to do something?" (30) How does Macdonald's views on White's book evolve over time?

3. Macdonald notes, "What we see in the lives of animals are lessons we've learned from the world." (60) Through closely observing her hawk's life, what lessons does Helen ultimately learn from the world?

4. After living several days with her hawk in her flat, Macdonald observes, "I was turning into a hawk." (85) What does Macdonald mean? How does she explain her "transformation"?

5. Macdonald writes that each picture her father took was "a record, a testament, a bulwark against forgetting, against nothingness, against death." (71) Later, she looks just once at the last photo her father took before he died. "[A]n empty London street…a wall tipped sideways from the vertical and running into the distance; a vanishing point of sallow, stormy sky." It is a photo that she can "never stop seeing." (106) Does Macdonald's memory of this photo serve as a bulwark against forgetting her father? Or against her father's death?

6. Macdonald writes about herself, "We carry the lives we've imagined as we carry the lives we have, and sometimes a reckoning comes of all the lives we have lost." (129) Later, she writes about White, "Sometimes a reckoning comes of all the lives we have lost, and sometimes we take it upon ourselves to burn them to ashes." (130) What is Macdonald's reckoning? White's? How do their respective hawks help or hinder their respective reckonings?

7. Macdonald writes, "Hunting with the hawk took me to the very edge of being a human." (195) What does Macdonald mean? How far to the edge does Macdonald go?

HOUSE OF THIEVES

Charles Belfoure

In 1886 New York, a respectable architect shouldn't have any connection to the notorious gang of thieves and killers that rules the underbelly of the city. But when John Cross's son racks up an unfathomable gambling debt to Kent's Gents, Cross must pay it back himself. All he has to do is use his inside knowledge of high society mansions and museums to craft a robbery even the smartest detectives won't solve. The take better include some cash, too—the bigger the payout, the faster this will be over.

With a newfound talent for sniffing out vulnerable and lucrative targets, Cross becomes invaluable to the gang. But Cross's entire life has become a balancing act, and it will only take one mistake for it all to come crashing down—and for his family to go down too.

"Belfoure's sly, roguish writing opens a window to those living both gilded and tarnished lives...Best of all, Belfoure holds together each and every thread of the novel, resulting in a most memorable, evocative read."
—***Publishers Weekly* STARRED Review**

"Charles Belfoure sees New York's Gilded Age with an architect's eye and evokes the atmosphere wonderfully." —**Edward Rutherford, *New York Times* bestselling author of *Paris: The Novel* and *New York: The Novel***

"Rich in mischief and populated by thieves and gamblers, gentry and rebels, it is as complex and ambitious as New York City itself. This is historical fiction at its best." —**Ariel Lawhon, author of *The Wife, the Maid, and the Mistress***

About the Author: **Charles Belfoure** is the internationally bestselling author of *The Paris Architect* and is an architect by profession, with a specialty in historical preservation. He graduated from the Pratt Institute and Columbia University, has been a freelance writer for the *Baltimore Sun* and *The New York Times*, and has written several architectural histories.

September 2015 | Hardcover | Fiction | 432 pp | $25.99 | ISBN 9781492617891
Sourcebooks | sourcebooks.com | charlesbelfoure.com

CONVERSATION STARTERS

1. In order to save his family, John Cross must do something he finds morally reprehensible. Would you resort to criminality to save your family from death?

2. This is a story about the double lives a family chooses to live. Which was your favorite?

3. Until 1914, Americans could ingest any drug they wanted, including dangerous drugs that are outlawed today. What did you think of Granny's preference for opium?

4. James T. Kent, a well- bred gentleman from a wealthy family, is a cold-blooded killer and gets an almost sexual satisfaction from committing crime. Was he a compelling villain?

5. New York high society had a very strict code of behavior that one had to obey or be banished. What did you think of that code? Why did that code devolve into the less-stringent rules of behavior we have today?

6. How does poverty in America today compare with that portrayed in the Gilded Age in New York City?

7. Homelessness is a great concern in our cities today. What did you think of the fact that about twenty thousand children roamed the streets of New York in the 1880s?

8. Cross's children form friendships with people they normally would never come into contact with. What did you like about Julia and Nolan's friendship? Charlie and Eddie's? George and Kitty's?

9. George's gambling addiction was the source of all the troubles. How did you feel about George and his illness? Were you angry with him?

10. Cross was devastated when he learned of his son's secret. What would you as a parent have been thinking and feeling?

THE INVENTION OF WINGS
Sue Monk Kidd

Hetty "Handful" Grimke, an urban slave in early nineteenth century Charleston, yearns for life beyond the suffocating walls that enclose her within the wealthy Grimke household. The Grimke's daughter, Sarah, has known from an early age she is meant to do something large in the world, but she is hemmed in by the limits imposed on women.

Kidd's sweeping novel is set in motion on Sarah's 11th birthday, when she is given ownership of ten-year-old Handful, who is to be her handmaid. We follow their remarkable journeys over the next thirty five years, as both strive for a life of their own, dramatically shaping each other's destinies and forming a complex relationship marked by guilt, defiance, estrangement and the uneasy ways of love. As the stories build to a riveting climax, Handful will endure loss and sorrow, finding courage and a sense of self in the process. Sarah will experience crushed hopes, betrayal, unrequited love, and ostracism before leaving Charleston to find her place alongside her fearless younger sister, Angelina, as one of the early pioneers in the abolition and women's rights movements.

Inspired by the historical figure of Sarah Grimke, Kidd goes beyond the record to flesh out the rich interior lives of all of her characters, both real and invented, including Handful's cunning mother, Charlotte, who courts danger in her search for something better. This exquisitely written novel is a triumph of storytelling that looks with unswerving eyes at a devastating wound in American history, through women whose struggles for liberation, empowerment, and expression will leave no reader unmoved.

"Exhilarating . . . powerful . . . By humanizing these formidable women, The Invention of Wings furthers our essential understanding of what has happened among us as Americans – and why it still matters." —**The Washington Post**

"If this isn't an American classic-to-be, I don't know what is . . . this book is as close to perfect as any I've ever read." —**The Dallas Morning News**

About the Author: **Sue Monk Kidd**'s novel, *The Secret Life of Bees*, has sold more than 3,500,000 copies. She is the author of several acclaimed memoirs and the recipient of the Poets & Writers award.

May 2015 | Trade Paperback | Fiction | 384 pp | $17.00 | ISBN 9780143121701
Penguin Books | penguinrandomhouse.com | suemonkkidd.com

CONVERSATION STARTERS

1. The title *The Invention of Wings* was one of the first inspirations that Sue Monk Kidd had as she began the novel. Why is the title an apt one for Kidd's novel? What are some of the ways that the author uses the imagery and symbolism of birds, wings, and flight?

2. After laying aside her aspirations to become a lawyer, Sarah remarks that the Graveyard of Failed Hopes is "an all-female establishment." What makes her say so? What was your experience of reading Kidd's portrayal of women's lives in the nineteenth century?

3. In what ways does Sarah struggle against the dictates of her family, society and religion? Can you relate to her need to break away from the life she had in order to create a new and unknown life? What sort of risk and courage does this call for?

4. Were you aware of the role that Sarah and Angelina Grimke played in abolition and women's rights? Have women's achievements in history been lost or overlooked? What do you think it takes to be a reformer today?

5. Kidd portrays an array of male characters in the novel: Sarah's father; Sarah's brother Thomas; Theodore Weld; Denmark Vesey; Goodis Grimke, Israel Morris, Burke Williams. Some of them are men of their time, some are ahead of their time. Which of these male characters did you find most compelling? What positive and negative roles did they play in Sarah and Handful's evolvement?

6. How does the spirit tree function in Handful's life? What do you think of the rituals and meanings surrounding it?

7. Had you heard of the Denmark Vesey slave plot before reading this novel? Were you aware of the extent that slaves resisted? Why do you think the myth of the happy, compliant slave endured? What were some of the more inventive or cunning ways that Charlotte, Handful and other characters rebelled and subverted the system?

8. *The Invention of Wings* takes the reader back to the roots of racism in America. How has slavery left its mark in American life? To what extent has the wound been healed? Do you think slavery has been a taboo topic in American life?

THE LAST PILOT
Benjamin Johncock

Jim Harrison is a test pilot in the U.S. Air Force, one of the exalted few. He spends his days cheating death in the skies above the Mojave Desert and his nights at his friend Pancho's bar, often with his wife, Grace. She and Harrison are secretly desperate for a child-and when, against all odds, Grace learns that she is pregnant, the two are overcome with joy.

While America becomes swept up in the fervor of the Space Race, Harrison turns his attention home, passing up the chance to become an astronaut to welcome his daughter into the world. But when his family is faced with a sudden and inexplicable tragedy, Harrison's instincts as a father and a pilot are put to the test.

The turns the Harrisons take together are at once astonishing and recognizable; their journey, both frightening and full of hope. Set against the backdrop of one of the most emotionally charged periods in American history, *The Last Pilot* is a mesmerizing debut novel of loss and finding courage in the face of it from an extraordinary new talent.

"Told in language as beautifully spare-and unsparing-as a desert or a moonscape, The Last Pilot *reminds us in powerful ways that the real unknown frontier still lies within the mysteries of the human heart."*
—**Kim Edwards, No. 1** *New York Times* **bestselling author of** *The Lake of Dreams*

"This is by far the best debut novel I've read in years . . . a Western in disguise; a quiet, limpid Western, where the action mostly takes place in the air and in the chambers of the heart. To me, it reads like the reclusive disciple of Cormac McCarthy and de Saint-Exupéry."—**Joanne Harris,** *New York Times* **bestselling author**

ABOUT THE AUTHOR: **Benjamin Johncock** resides in England and writes regularly for *The Guardian*. *The Last Pilot* is his first novel.

July 2015 | Trade Paperback | Fiction | 320 pp | $26.00 | ISBN 9781250066640
Picador | us.macmillan.com | benjohncock.com

CONVERSATION STARTERS

1. Benjamin Johncock provides readers with wonderful, atmospheric descriptions of the desert landscape. Why do you think he dedicates so much space to describing the land?

2. Pancho is one of the novel's most colorful characters and is based on real-life figure, Florence Lowe "Pancho" Barnes. In what ways is Pancho a woman ahead of her time?

3. Why does Grace keep her visits with Reverend Irving a secret from Jim?

4. *The Last Pilot* is framed by historical events: the Cold War, the Cuban Missile Crisis, and the Space Race. How does this historical context affect your reading of the novel? Are you drawn to novels that are based on true stories?

5. After Florence is born, Jim begins to learn what it means to be a parent. Johncock writes, "Florence cried hard when hungry and it cut into him, not the volume, or the sound, but the need." What was it about this situation that Jim didn't like?

6. After Jim is told the terrible news about Florence's brain tumor he still insists on going through with his scheduled flight test even though Riley urges him to "call it a day." Why do you think Jim insists on going through with the flight test? What insights into Jim's character does this scene provide?

7. Do you think Jim would have made the decision to join NASA's lunar landing mission if Florence had lived?

8. During the height of the Cuban Missile Crisis, Grace asks Jim to stay with her instead of continuing to devote all of his time to the space program. When he refuses, she asks him if he thinks the program is more important than her, to which he replies, yes. Do you agree with Jim? Why or why not?

9. As Jim's mental state begins to unravel, he starts to believe that he killed Florence. Do you place any blame on Jim for Florence's death?

10. The novel ends on Christmas Eve, 1968. Jim and Grace are watching a broadcast from the Apollo 8 mission whose crew is the first to see the entire Earth from space. Why do you think Johncock ends with this powerful image?

LIAR, TEMPTRESS, SOLDIER, SPY

Four Women Undercover in the Civil War

Karen Abbott

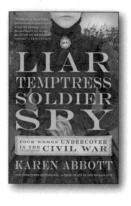

Seventeen-year-old Belle Boyd, an avowed rebel with a dangerous temper, shot a Union soldier in her home, and became a courier and spy for the Confederate army, using her considerable charms to seduce men on both sides. Emma Edmonds disguised herself as a man to enlist as a Union private named Frank Thompson, witnessing the bloodiest battles of the war and infiltrating enemy lines. The beautiful widow Rose O'Neal Greenhow engaged in affairs with powerful Northern politicians, and used her young daughter to send information to Southern generals. Elizabeth Van Lew, a wealthy Richmond abolitionist, hid behind her proper Southern manners as she orchestrated a far-reaching espionage ring—even placing a former slave inside the Confederate White House—right under the noses of increasingly suspicious rebel detectives.

With a cast of real-life characters, including Nathaniel Hawthorne, General Stonewall Jackson, Detective Allan Pinkerton, Abraham and Mary Todd Lincoln, and Emperor Napoléon III, *Liar, Temptress, Soldier, Spy* shines a dramatic new light on these daring—and, until now, unsung—heroines.

"With this book, Karen Abbott declares herself the John le Carré of Civil War espionage—with the added benefit that the saga she tells is all true and beautifully researched." —**Erik Larson, bestselling author of** *Devil in the White City*

"A gripping page-turner that moves at a breathtaking clip through the dramatic events of the Civil War." —**Los Angeles Times**

"Engrossing . . . Liar, Temptress, Soldier, Spy *is conscientiously researched and smoothly written and structured."* —**Wall Street Journal**

ABOUT THE AUTHOR: **Karen Abbott** is the *New York Times* bestselling author of *Sin in the Second City* and *American Rose*. She has written for the *New York Times Book Review, Wall Street Journal, Smithsonian* magazine, *Salon*, and other publications.

September 2015 | Trade Paperback | Nonfiction | 544 pp | $16.99 | ISBN 9780062092908
Harper Perennial | harpercollins.com | karenabbott.net

CONVERSATION STARTERS

1. *Liar, Temptress, Soldier, Spy* examines how women's roles changed when the men in their lives enlisted in the Civil War. What was the most difficult aspect of being a woman during this time? Do you think most women considered their increased responsibilities a hardship or a freedom?

2. The women defy traditional gender roles many times. How does each character use her femininity to achieve her goals? What did President Lincoln's advisor mean when he lamented the proliferation of "fashionable female spies?"

3. Emma Edmonds disguised herself to enlist in the Union army. How do you think Emma (and ~400 more) pulled off this feat? What challenges come with living as imposters among men?

4. Discuss the title. How does it apply to each character? When and how was each a liar, a temptress, a soldier, and a spy?

5. Belle, Rose, and Elizabeth all employed servants/slaves during their espionage missions. Compare and contrast their treatment of servants/slaves. Did any of their views evolve?

6. Elizabeth's servant Mary Jane Bowser is a key character. How does being African American affect her role as a spy? How did it make her job easier, or more difficult?

7. Discuss each character's relationships with men. How did the women use men to their advantage? Were the women ever used themselves?

8. Belle looked up to Rose. Compare and contrast them. In your opinion, who was more successful? How did Belle's reputation as a "fast girl" affect her work for the Confederacy?

9. Rose's daughter is crucial in Rose's espionage work. Was she justified in using her daughter? Would you have done the same?

10. Which spy did you relate to the most? Why? What motivated each woman? Had you lived during the Civil War, would you have dared to be a spy?

11. Both North and South spoke of "atrocities" committed by the enemy. Which atrocity was the most shocking to you? Did one side exaggerate more?

LIBRARY OF SOULS
Ransom Riggs

Time is running out for the peculiar children. With a dangerous madman on the loose and their beloved Miss Peregrine still in danger, Jacob Portman and Emma Bloom are forced to stage the most daring of rescue missions. They'll travel through a war-torn landscape, meet new allies, and face greater dangers than ever. . . . Will Jacob come into his own as the hero his fellow peculiars know him to be? This action-packed adventure features more than 50 all-new peculiar photographs.

Praise for the Miss Peregrine's Peculiar Children Series

"Readers looking for the next Harry Potter may want to visit Miss Peregrine's Home for Peculiar Children." —**CNN**

"Riggs deftly moves between fantasy and reality, prose and photography to create an enchanting and at times positively terrifying story." —**Associated Press**

"What makes the series soar, however, is not the world-building, as intriguing as it is, but the heartfelt intensity of the emotions." —**Virginian-Pilot**

"Ideal for fans of Neil Gaiman and Daniel Kraus, Hollow City blends fantasy and horror into a world that will engross readers and leave them eager for more." —**Shelf Awareness for Readers**

ABOUT THE AUTHOR: **Ransom Riggs** is the author of *Miss Peregrine's Home for Peculiar Children* (Quirk, 2011), a *New York Times* best seller that has sold more than 2 million copies, as well as its best-selling sequel, *Hollow City* (Quirk, 2013). Translation rights have been sold to more than 25 territories worldwide. He lives in Santa Monica, California, with his wife.

September 2015 | Hardcover | Fiction | 400 pp | $18.99 | ISBN 9781594747588
Quirk Books | quirkbooks.com | ransomriggs.com

CONVERSATION STARTERS

1. At the end of *Hollow City* Jacob discovers his peculiar ability, and in *Library of Souls* he must learn to master this power in order to save his friends and beloved Miss Peregrine. Were you surprised by Jacob's lack of confidence in himself? How well do you think he handled the pressure he was under?

2. At the beginning of *Library of Souls*, Jacob, Emma, and Addison find themselves in present-day London. This is the first time Emma is encountering the modern world. What do you think it must have been like for her to encounter the London Underground and a comic con?

3. In *Hollow City* the wights posed as Nazi soldiers, and in *Library of Souls* they pose as police officers. What do you think of this pattern of wights portraying authority figures?

4. Devil's Acre is a miserable loop, filled with depravity and criminal activity, and the only way for Jacob, Emma, and Addison to get there is via Sharon's boat. What were your first impressions of Sharon?

5. Riggs introduces a lot of new peculiar characters in *Library of Souls*. Which is your favorite peculiar, and is there a peculiar ability you would want for yourself?

6. Jacob is badly hurt and loses consciousness. When he wakes up he finds himself in the house of Bentham, Miss Peregine's other brother. Were you surprised to learn that Miss Peregrine has another brother?

7. Bentham reveals that Jacob is the key to Caul's evil plan. Did this surprise you? Why do you think Caul kidnapped Miss Peregrine, if Jacob was indeed the key all along?

8. How did you react when you finally learned what the library of souls was? How did it differ from what you imagined?

9. In the library of souls we learn that Bentham is not who he originally seemed to be. In the end, Miss Peregrine has to make a difficult decision to protect the peculiars. What was your reaction to her actions against her brothers?

10. *Library of Souls* is the end of Jacob's story arc in the Peculiar Children series. Are you satisfied with how Riggs ends Jacob's story? What do you think will happen next?

ME BEFORE YOU
Jojo Moyes

Louisa Clark is an ordinary girl living an exceedingly ordinary life—steady boyfriend, close family—who has barely been farther afield than their tiny village. She takes a badly needed job working for ex–Master of the Universe Will Traynor, who is wheelchair bound after an accident. Will has always lived a huge life—big deals, extreme sports, worldwide travel—and now he's pretty sure he cannot live the way he is. Will is acerbic, moody, bossy—but Lou refuses to treat him with kid gloves, and soon his happiness means more to her than she expected.

A Love Story for this generation, *Me Before You* brings to life two people who couldn't have less in common—a heartbreakingly romantic novel that asks, What do you do when making the person you love happy also means breaking your own heart?

AFTER YOU: The sequel to *Me Before You*

Dear Reader, I wasn't going to write a sequel to *Me Before You*. But for years, readers kept asking and I kept wondering what Lou did with her life. In the end the idea came, as they sometimes do, at 5:30 in the morning, leaving me sitting bolt upright in my bed and scrambling for my pen.

It has been such a pleasure revisiting Lou and her family, and the Traynors, and confronting them with a whole new set of issues. As ever, they have made me laugh, and cry. I hope readers feel the same way at meeting them—especially Lou—again. And I'm hoping that those who love Will will find plenty to enjoy.

ABOUT THE AUTHOR: **Jojo Moyes** writes for the *Daily Telegraph*, *Daily Mail*, *Red and Woman* & *Home*. She lives with her husband and three children on a farm in Essex, England.

Me Before You
July 2013 | Trade Paperback | Fiction | 416 pp | $16.00 | ISBN 9780143124542
Penguin Books | penguinrandomhouse.com | jojomoyes.com

After You
September 2015 | Hardcover | Fiction | 368 pp | $26.95 | ISBN 9780525426592
Pamela Dorman Books | penguinrandomhouse.com | jojomoyes.com

CONVERSATION STARTERS

1. If you were Louisa, would you have quit working for the Traynors? If yes, at what point?

2. Were you able to relate to the way Will felt after his accident? What about his outlook on life did you find most difficult to understand or accept?

3. Discuss the meaning of the novel's title. To whom do the "me" and "you" refer?

4. Louisa often finds Mrs. Traynor cold and judgmental. Is there an appropriate way to behave in Mrs. Traynor's situation?

5. What is your opinion of Mr. Traynor? Did it change after you read his side of the story?

6. Why is Louisa able to reach Will when so many others could not?

7. Were you as surprised as Lou to learn of Will's plans?

8. Compare Louisa's relationship with Treena to Will's relationship with Georgina. Do siblings know one another any better simply because they are related?

9. Would Patrick have asked Louisa to move in with him if he hadn't felt threatened by Will? If Louisa had never accepted her job with the Traynors, where would her relationship with Patrick have gone?

10. Discuss Louisa's own secret ties to the castle. Would most girls in her situation have blamed themselves? Should Treena have behaved differently in the aftermath?

11. What did you make of the way Lou's mother, Josie, judges Lou's decisions regarding Will. Is Josie's reaction fair?

12. Before his accident, Will was a philanderer and a corporate raider who would probably never have given Louisa a second look. Why is it that people are so often unable to see what's truly important until they've experienced loss?

THE MEURSAULT INVESTIGATION
Kamel Daoud

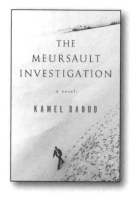

He was the brother of "the Arab" killed by the infamous Meursault, the antihero of Camus's classic novel. Seventy years after that event, Harun, who has lived since childhood in the shadow of his sibling's memory, refuses to let him remain anonymous: he gives his brother a story and a name—Musa—and describes the events that led to Musa's casual murder on a dazzlingly sunny beach.

In a bar in Oran, night after night, Harun ruminates on his solitude, on his broken heart, on his anger with men desperate for a god, and on his disarray when faced with a country that has so disappointed him. A stranger among his own people, he wants to be granted, finally, the right to die.

The Stranger is of course central to Daoud's story, in which he both endorses and criticizes one of the most famous novels in the world. A worthy complement to its great predecessor, *The Meursault Investigation* is not only a profound meditation on Arab identity and the disastrous effects of colonialism in Algeria, but also a stunning work of literature in its own right, told in a unique and affecting voice.

"*A tour-de-force reimagining of Camus's* The Stranger, *from the point of view of the mute Arab victims.*" —**The New Yorker**

"*[A] rich and inventive new novel…so convincing and so satisfying that we no longer think of the original story as the truth, but rather come to question it.*" —**New York Times Book Review**

"The Meursault Investigation *is an instant classic.*" —**The Guardian** (UK)

ABOUT THE AUTHOR: **Kamel Daoud** is an Algerian journalist based in Oran. A finalist for the Prix Goncourt, *The Meursault Investigation* won the Goncourt Prize for First Novel, the Prix François Mauriac, and the Prix des Cinq-Continents de la francophonie. A feature film is slated for release in 2017.

June 2015 | Trade Paperback | Fiction | 160 pp | $14.95 | ISBN 9781590517512
Other Press | otherpress.com

CONVERSATION STARTERS

1. Describe the relationship that emerges between Harun and his mother after Musa's murder. Is it comparable to how Musa describes the power organized religion holds over the imaginations of his countrymen? (See "She seemed to resent me for a death I basically refused to undergo ... Maman knew the art of making ghosts live and, conversely, was very good at annihilating her close relatives" (36–37); "My body, therefore, became the visible *trace* of her dead son, and I ended up obeying her unspoken injunction" (41); "[The imam] wasn't even sure he was alive, because he was living like a dead man" (141).

2. Why does Musa learn French? What does he appreciate about French and the way Camus/Meursault uses it that he does not find in how Maman uses language? In the story, Maman holds an enormous amount of power over Harun. When he learns to read and write in French, does that power dynamic change?

3. Harun says, "What hurts me every time I think about it is that [Meursault] killed [Musa] by passing over him, not by shooting him" (5). Describe the power that Meursault's account of the murder, as opposed to the murder itself, has on Harun's family and the course of his life.

4. One of Harun's criticisms of his mother is how her language is "not too big on precision" (37). What else is Maman imprecise about, and how does her imprecision shape Harun's life?

5. Harun explains that because of the popularity of Meursault's account, his brother Musa "over and over again . . . replays his own death" (3). What else recurs in the novel? In the end, is this cycle of recurrence something that can be broken?

6. Meriem is one of the many characters in the novel who "disappears," yet Harun never refers to her as such. Why do you think that is?

7. Does *The Meursault Investigation* have a Musa of its own—a character or characters who are afforded nothing more than anonymity? Does this anonymity have the same violence as the anonymity of "the Arab" in *The Stranger*?

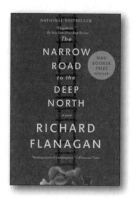

THE NARROW ROAD TO THE DEEP NORTH

Richard Flanagan

Man Booker Prize Winner
A Best Books of the Year: *The New York Times,*
NPR, The Washington Post, The Minneapolis
Star-Tribune, The Economist, The Seattle Times,
Financial Times

August, 1943: Australian surgeon Dorrigo Evans is haunted by his affair with his uncle's young wife two years earlier. His life, in a brutal Japanese POW camp on the Thai-Burma Death Railway, is a daily struggle to save the men under his command. Until he receives a letter that will change him forever.

A savagely beautiful novel about the many forms of good and evil, of truth and transcendence, as one man comes of age, prospers, only to discover all that he has lost.

"Some years, very good books win the Man Booker Prize, but this year a masterpiece has won it." —**A.C. Grayling, Chair of Judges, Man Booker Prize 2014**

"Richard Flanagan has written a sort of Australian War and Peace.*"* —**Alan Cheuse, NPR**

"A symphony of tenderness and love, a moving and powerful story that captures the weight and breadth of a life . . . A masterpiece." —**The Guardian**

ABOUT THE AUTHOR: **Richard Flanagan** is the author of five previous novels—*Death of a River Guide, The Sound of One Hand Clapping, Gould's Book of Fish, The Unknown Terrorist,* and *Wanting*—which have received numerous honors and have been published in twenty-six countries. He lives in Tasmania.

April 2015 | Trade Paperback | Fiction | 416 pp | $15.95 | ISBN 9780804171472
Vintage | penguinrandomhouse.com | richardflanagan.com

CONVERSATION STARTERS

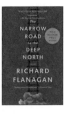

1. What is the significance of the name of the novel, *The Narrow Road to the Deep North*? Why might Flanagan have chosen to name his book after Basho's well-known travelogue by the same name?

2. How does the author's "visual" portrait of the characters and the places they inhabit inform us about the state of the characters and shape our reaction to their story? Evaluate Flanagan's choice of imagery and language. What type of imagery and language is most prevalent in the book? Does Flanagan employ much symbolism? How does this ultimately shape our experience of the book and our understanding of the major themes addressed therein?

3. The POWs are put to work—often to their deaths—as slaves building a railway for the Japanese emperor. What does this railway represent to the Japanese people and their leader? Why are they so devoted to its construction that they can be driven to violence and murder to ensure its completion? Nakamura says that the English also utilized "non-freedom" in order to ensure progress in their own country. What does this seem to indicate about the nature of progress and how do his comments change our perception of both the European and the Asian characters and what is happening on the Line?

4. Evaluate Flanagan's depiction of the dual nature of man. Consider representations of good and evil, of man as philosopher-poet and man as animal, of the public and private self. Does it seem to be possible for man to resist this dual nature? Does the novel indicate whether man can choose which side of his dual nature prevails over the other or is this beyond man's control?

5. Are there any representations of faith in the novel? If so, to what are the characters faithful? There are also many examples of faithlessness and unfaithfulness to be found in the book. What causes the characters to lose their faith or to be unfaithful?

6. At the conclusion of the story, Flanagan presents us with the image of Dorrigo opening a book only to find out that the final pages have been torn out. Why do you think that the author chooses to employ this image at the story's end?

OLD HEART
Peter Ferry

Tom Johnson has turned 85 and has suffered a few "events," though he knows his mind is still sharp. His adult children want to move him out of the homestead lake house and into a retirement home. But Tom resists in a most clever way. He slips away from his remaining family and sets out to find the only woman he ever loved, a woman he met in the Netherlands where he was stationed during World War II.

Old Heart is an unsentimental novel about forgiveness, a sense of home and all the remaining rights of an old man.

"Ferry presents and proves the bold and needed idea that it's never too late to re-open the past to recast the present." —**Dave Eggers**

"Peter Ferry's writing is wry and beautiful, and this exuberant novel shows how a man driven by love can add a surprising extra chapter to his life." —**Elizabeth McKenzie**

"A life-affirming novel about love and second chances; the rights, integrity, and freedom of the elderly; and the toll of mistakes and disappointments." —***Publishers Weekly***

"This is a novel of love and of loss and of self-determination. Old Heart moves through time and grabs your interest on every page and will stay with you for keeps." —***The Chicago Tribune***

"Peter Ferry crafts a wise and delicate novel of aging, love and autonomy in Old Heart. … The result is delightfully warm and universally appealing." —***Shelf Awareness***

About the Author: **Peter Ferry** is the author of the 2008 novel *Travel Writing*. His stories have appeared in *McSweeneys, Fiction, StoryQuarterly, OR* and *Chicago Quarterly Review*. He is the recipient of an Illinois Arts Council Award for Short Fiction and is a frequent contributor to the travel pages of *The Chicago Tribune* and WorldHum.com.

June 2015 | Trade Paperback | Fiction | 256 pp | $16.00 | ISBN 9781609531171
Unbridled Books | unbridledbooks.com | peterferrywrites.com

CONVERSATION STARTERS

Old Heart

A novel

Peter Ferry

1. What is Tom Johnson afraid of? What is he not afraid of?

2. Is the gamble Tom takes in running away from home reasonable? Is it realistic?

3. In the last fifty years the life expectancy of Down syndrome people has more than doubled from about twenty-five years to more than fifty years. While advances in medicine account for some of the change, the main causes appear to be social. As late as 1960, people with Down syndrome were routinely institutionalized usually at the age of six. In the years since, however, it has become increasingly common for them to continue living at home with their families, to go to school and to work in their own communities. In fact, that's now the norm. What does this change say about our society?

4. The author says that Nora started out as a device to keep Tom informed of events at home, but she developed into one of the voices in the novel. What is it that takes her from being only a device and makes her into a character?

5. Tom says that Tony saved his soul (68). What do you think he means by this?

6. What do you make of Pim's question, "Isn't what you think you see what you see?" (217).

7. Tom describes his relationship with Pim as existing "at the confluence of imagination, memory and perception" (242). What do you think he is saying in that line?

8. In the front of *Old Heart*, Athene MacGruder who is eighty-five says, "You think I was always old, don't you? Well I wasn't." Why did the author pick that epigraph for his book, and how does it inform the novel?

9. Would you describe the relationships between parents and their children or grandchildren in *Old Heart* as realistic?

10. The second epigraph in the front of *Old Heart* is a haiku that reads, "Behold the summer grass,/All that remains of the/Dreams of warriors." What could these lines mean?

ORHAN'S INHERITANCE
Aline Ohanesian

A #1 Indie Next Pick
A *Library Journal* Editor's Pick
A B&N Discover Great New Writers Selection

When Orhan's brilliant and eccentric grandfather, who built a dynasty out of making kilim rugs, is found dead, submerged in a vat of dye, Orhan inherits the decades-old business. But his grandfather has left the family estate to a stranger thousands of miles away, Seda, an aging woman in a retirement home in Los Angeles. Over time, Orhan begins to unearth the story that eighty-seven-year-old Seda so closely guards--a story that, if it's told, has the power to undo the legacy upon which Orhan's family is built and could unravel Orhan's own future.

Moving between the last years of the Ottoman Empire and the 1990s, *Orhan's Inheritance* is a story of passionate love, unspeakable horrors, incredible resilience, and the hidden stories that haunt a family.

"A remarkable debut novel that exhibits an impressive grasp of history as well as narrative intensity and vivid prose." —Minneapolis Star Tribune

"Rich, tragic, compelling, and realized with deep care and insight." —Elle

"A breathtaking and expansive work of historical fiction and proof that the past can sometimes rewrite the future." —**Christina Baker Kline, author of** *Orphan Train*

"A harrowing tale of unimaginable sacrifice . . . A novel that delves into the darkest corners of human history and emerges with a tenuous sense of hope." —***Kirkus Reviews*, starred review**

ABOUT THE AUTHOR: **Aline Ohanesian** is a grandchild of Armenian Genocide survivors. Their story was the inspiration for her first novel, *Orhan's Inheritance*, which was a finalist for the PEN/Bellwether Prize for Socially Engaged Fiction. She lives in San Juan Capistrano, CA, with her husband and two children.

April 2015 | Hardcover | Fiction | 352 pp | $25.95 | ISBN 9781616203740
January 2016 | Trade Paperback | Fiction | 352 pp | $15.95 | ISBN 9781616205300
Algonquin Books | algonquin.com | alineohanesian.com

CONVERSATION STARTERS

1. Setting plays such a significant role in *Orhan's Inheritance*. How do the two settings, Karod village in Turkey and the Ararat Home in Los Angeles, affect the characters?

2. Why do you think Kemal dies the way he does? What is the symbolism of the vat of dye?

3. Orhan's early photography was so focused on abstraction that he failed to see the world around him clearly. How does Orhan's early photography compare with his later work, when he takes up the camera again? In what way does he see the world differently?

4. Do you think words construct meaning differently than visual images do, whether drawn or photographed?

5. How are Orhan and Seda similar when it comes to their relationship with their pasts? What is Ani's perspective on the past? What do you think these characters learn from one another?

6. Lucine's father, Hairig, defines strength as adaptability. How would you describe Lucine's strength? What are the qualities that help her survive this ordeal?

7. At what point does Seda stop speaking? Why do you think she makes this choice?

8. Do your feelings about Fatma change in the course of the novel? If so, how?

9. Why does Lucine feel that she and Kemal can never be together?

10. There are many instances of individual and collective guilt in the story as exemplified in the war scenes with Kemal and his soldier friends. Do you think there's such a thing as collective guilt? If so, is it easier to bear and what are its effects?

11. Once Orhan knows about his family's and country's history, how do you think he should respond? Do you think he's done enough by the end of the novel?

12. Much of the novel grapples with the power of words as well as their insufficiency. How important are the words we use to describe someone or something? Why does it matter what Orhan calls Fatma or whether we call what happened in 1915 a genocide?

PRINCIPLES OF NAVIGATION
Lynn Sloan

In a small town in Indiana, Alice Becotte wants desperately what should be simple: a baby. What Alice's husband, Rolly, wants is time for his art. He's a talented sculptor with ambitions that draw him away from his steady teaching gig at a "backwater" college. Alice, the lone full-time reporter for their local, struggling newspaper, isn't as invested in her career. The crack in their marriage widens when, finally pregnant, the pair face devastating news.

It's 1999, a time when the world is afraid of falling apart once the new millennium arrives. Told from both character's points of view, this haunting novel offers readers a complex, surprising, and memorable story about a couple's struggle as their worlds threaten to collapse. When each partner is tested and found wanting, they forge a new way forward, without map or compass, guided only by fragile and fleeting glimpses of grace.

Praise for *Principles of Navigation*

" . . . *a tender, thoughtful story of a couple whose once happy marriage dissolves amidst the stress of infertility and infidelity—and unmet expectations. . . . quietly compelling. It is by no means a heart-pounding page-turner, but it is a page-turner nonetheless, a subtle story that gnaws and needles long after the cover is closed.* "—**Chicago Book Review**

" . . . *an annunciation, a miracle, . . . this novel of generation, of stasis, and of transformation.*"—**Newcity**

" . . . *fascinating and gripping.*"—**Centered on Books**

ABOUT THE AUTHOR: **Lynn Sloan**'s first career was as a photographer. Her fine art photographs have been exhibited nationally and internationally. Her stories have appeared in numerous literary journals and been nominated for a Pushcart Prize. She grew up as an Air Force brat, settled in the Midwest, and now lives outside Chicago. *Principles of Navigation* is her debut novel.

February 2015 | Trade Paperback | Fiction | 294 pp | $15.00 | ISBN 9781937677930
Fomite Press | fomitepress.com | lynnsloan.com

CONVERSATION STARTERS

1. Many couples have trouble conceiving. Lynn Sloan uses this particular couple's struggle as a lens through which to address questions of marriage and family. How is marriage presented in the novel? What does the book suggest about families?

2. Neither Alice or Rolly are religious, but Alice finds solace in her connection to the Virgin Mary. Why? How do the religious scenes work to advance the story?

3. Why is it important to the novel that it is set in 1999?

4. Do you think Rolly's choice of using ships in his art is symbolic?

5. Discuss the mothers in this novel.

6. Why does the novel have the title it does?

7. Sometimes Alice thinks of her life in terms of stories and headlines. Is she self-absorbed or is this a way of processing her pain or is this simply how she has been trained to think? Does it diminish her pain when presented as a headline, offering distance? Is this a commentary on how journalists respond to the people about whom they write?

8. Why do you think the author chose to set this novel in a rural environment?

9. Alice is scornful of her mother's decision to remarry. Her mother wants Alice and Rolly to stay together. Why do they each have a stake in each other's marriages?

10. Part of the novel is about the commerce of art and the teaching of art. Does the competitive nature of his career affect Rolly's ability to produce good art?

11. Alice is critical of Rolly's work—his "baby," so to speak. Do you think Alice understands that Rolly, too, is trying to "birth" something?

12. By the end of the book, have your opinions about Alice and Rolly changed?

13. Do you think there is a healing in the end of the story? Is there forgiveness? What about hope?

14. The cover is striking. What scene do you think inspired it?

THE READERS OF BROKEN WHEEL RECOMMEND
Katarina Bivald

Once you let a book into your life, the most unexpected things can happen . . .

Broken Wheel, Iowa, has never seen anyone like Sara, who traveled all the way from Sweden just to meet her book-loving pen pal. When she arrives, however, she finds Amy's funeral guests just leaving. The residents of Broken Wheel are happy to look after their bewildered visitor—not much else to do in a small town that's almost beyond repair. They just never imagined that she'd start a bookstore. Or that books could bring them together—and change everything.

"This heartwarming story is the answer for those who loved The Storied Life of A.J. Fikry. Book lovers will applaud Sara and her love of books. Book clubs will delight in this delightful caper through book-loving middle America. Read this and smile!" —**Nancy Simpson-Brice, Book Vault (Oskaloosa, IA)**

"Every word on every page is sheer perfection...I'll carry this book in my heart for years to come." —**Bess Bleyaert, McLean & Eakin (Petoskey, MI)**

"LOVED IT! Readers will cheer for Sara and all the residents of Broken Wheel as a friendship that began with An Old Fashioned Girl renews and offers hope to an entire town." —**Jennifer Winberry, Hunterdon County Library (Flemington, NJ)**

ABOUT THE AUTHOR: **Katrina Bivald** lives outside of Stockholm, Sweden. This is her first novel. She grew up working part-time in a bookshop.

January 2016 | Trade Paperback | Fiction | 400 pp | $16.99 | ISBN 9781492623441
Sourcebooks | sourcebooks.com | katarinabivald.se/en/

CONVERSATION STARTERS

1. Sara and Amy develop a close relationship through exchanging letters. Have you ever had a pen pal? How might a friendship conducted entirely through writing be different than an in-person relationship?

2. Even though we never meet Amy in person, we get to know her through her letters to Sara. How did her letters influence your understanding of Amy and Sara's relationship?

3. Broken Wheel is a dying town, and a bookstore brings it back to life. How accurately do you think *The Readers of Broken Wheel Recommend* portrays small town America? Have you ever been to or lived in a place like Broken Wheel?

4. There is a strong rivalry between Broken Wheel and Hope. How do you think the residents of Hope viewed the people of Broken Wheel? How were their perceptions changed once the bookstore opened?

5. Sara arranged the books in her shop through unconventional genre names, including "Sex, Violence and Weapons" and "For Friday Nights and Lazy Sundays." What are some creative categories you might use to group your favorite books together?

6. Why do you think Sara was so reluctant to return to Sweden? What was missing from her life that she found in Broken Wheel?

7. How did you feel about the progression of Sara and Tom's relationship? Were you happy with the status of their relationship at the end of the book?

8. Why do you think Caroline and Josh felt so much pressure to keep their relationship a secret?

9. *The Readers of Broken Wheel Recommend* focuses on how books can change lives. How have books affected your life? Is there one book in particular that changed the way you see the world?

10. If you were to open a bookstore, what are some of the books you would absolutely have to have for sale?

11. Where do you think Sara, Tom, and the rest of the residents in Broken Wheel will be in five years? What do you think will have changed, and what will stay the same?

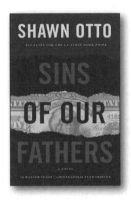

SINS OF OUR FATHERS
Shawn Lawrence Otto

John White, aka JW, is a small-town banker who teaches his associates how to profit from American Indian casino deposits while avoiding risk. But after embezzling funds to support his gambling addiction, JW is blackmailed by his boss into sabotaging a competing, Native American-owned bank. As JW befriends the family he is trying to frame, his plan to escape his past becomes more dangerous than he could have imagined.

Set in the backwoods of Northern Minnesota's Iron Range, *Sins of Our Fathers* is a gripping tale of loss, power, and the ultimate price of the American Dream.

Finalist for the L.A. Times Book Prize in the Mystery/Thriller category

"An unflinching look at America's original sin." —**Attica Locke, author of Black Water Rising**

"A wonderfully vivid debut." —***Publishers Weekly* (starred)**

"A literary tour de force and a psychological thriller that hooked me from the first page and carried me through to its stunning conclusion." —**Joel Surnow, creator of 24**

"A master class… One key to the effectiveness of Otto's novel is how cannily he shows the ages-old exploitative methods at work today." —***Minneapolis Star Tribune***

"Believable characters and a strong sense of place mark this tale of risk and redemption." —***Booklist***

"Excellent writing and dynamic characters make this novel a page turner that stands above the rest." —**Robert Alexander, author of *The Kitchen Boy***

ABOUT THE AUTHOR: **Shawn Lawrence Otto** is the writer and co-producer of the Oscar-nominated film *House of Sand and Fog*. He writes for television's top studios and his work has also appeared in *Rolling Stone*, *Science*, and *Salon*, among other publications. He lives in Marine on Saint Croix, MN.

September 2015 | Trade Paperback | Fiction | 368 pp | $16.95 | ISBN 9781571311184
Milkweed Editions | milkweed.org | shawnotto.com

CONVERSATION STARTERS

SHAWN OTTO

1. JW is a banker and a gambling addict. What are the similarities and differences between the two? Are JW's risks in both domains as calculated as he believes?

2. *Sins of Our Fathers* is a crime novel on several levels. What are the different crimes at play here? Who are the criminals? Do all these crimes involve breaking the law?

3. Both JW and Johnny had careers in the banking industry, have troubled relationships with their children, and lost their wives. How have these similar paths affected them differently? How do these similarities affect the development of their relationship?

4. In what ways are Johnny and Jacob "between worlds," not fully accepted in either the white or Native communities? Does this shift throughout the novel? How do they each respond to the pressure to act "more Indian"?

5. One of the most suggestive objects in the novel is the Chief Onepapa bill, which Johnny keeps locked in his safe. What does this symbol represent, both for Johnny personally and for the novel as a whole?

6. Throughout the novel, JW tries to reconcile his sense of what is right and wrong with his impulse to protect his own interests. How do you think he defines redemption at these different points in the novel: when he tries to win Carol back; when he helps Jorgensen with his plan; when he begins his relationship with Lola; when he sets fire to the money?

7. Shawn Otto describes *Sins of Our Fathers* as an exploration of "race, money, and the American Dream." How are these three elements intertwined? How does the novel explore the implications of their association?

8. In the novel, JW and Johnny often reflect on the decisions they've made as fathers. The intimate relationship between these men and their children is set against a larger legacy of dishonest land deals and Indian boarding schools. How do the characters grapple with the ramifications of their own actions, as well as the heritage created by generations of government policies?

SOME LUCK
Jane Smiley

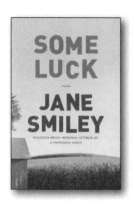

National Book Award Nominee
A Best Book of the Year: The Washington Post, NPR, USA Today, San Francisco Chronicle, Financial Times, The Seattle Times, St. Louis Post-Dispatch, BookPage

1920, Denby, Iowa: Rosanna and Walter Langdon have just welcomed their firstborn son, Frank, into their family farm. He will be the oldest of five.

Each chapter in this extraordinary novel covers a single year, encompassing the sweep of history as the Langdons abide by time-honored values and pass them on to their children. With the country on the cusp of enormous social and economic change through the early 1950s, we watch as the personal and the historical merge seamlessly: one moment electricity is just beginning to power the farm, and the next a son is volunteering to fight the Nazis. Later still, a girl we'd seen growing up now has a little girl of her own.

The first volume of an epic trilogy from a beloved writer at the height of her powers, *Some Luck* starts us on a literary adventure through cycles of birth and death, passion and betrayal that will span a century in America.

"[Smiley] seemingly writes the way her idol Dickens did—as easily as if it were breathing." —The New York Times

ABOUT THE AUTHOR: **Jane Smiley** is the author of numerous novels, including *A Thousand Acres*, which was awarded the Pulitzer Prize, as well as five works of nonfiction and a series of books for young adults. In 2001 she was inducted into the American Academy of Arts and Letters, and in 2006 she received the PEN USA Lifetime Achievement Award for Literature. She lives in northern California.

July 2015 | Trade Paperback | Fiction | 416 pp | $15.95 | ISBN 9780307744807
Anchor | penguinrandomhouse.com

CONVERSATION STARTERS

SOME
LUCK

JANE
SMILEY

1. What do you think the title means? Whose luck does it refer to? Is it only good or bad luck, or does the word "luck" shift in connotation as the novel goes forward?

2. Each chapter in the novel takes place over the course of one year. How does Smiley use this structure to propel her story?

3. How does Mary Elizabeth's death affect Rosanna? How does it change her relationship with the children who follow?

4. Throughout the story, Frank is described as persistent, if not outright stubborn. How does this quality help him in his life? Does it hinder him?

5. Over the course of the three decades *Some Luck* spans, various characters embrace or resist new technology—Walter and the tractor, Rosanna and electricity, Joey's farming techniques, Frank's study of German warfare. How does Smiley use their reactions to deepen our understanding of these characters and to show the passage of time?

6. What does Walter think and feel during the scene at the well? What do his decisions at that moment say about his own personality and the circumstances of the times? Why doesn't he tell Rosanna about it until many years later?

7. What role do faith and religion play in the early parts of the novel? What about for the subsequent generation? Would you say that religion is related to the theme of luck?

8. How do the generations of men engage differently in the wars of their times? What does their involvement show about their respective personalities, the nature of war, and America's evolving role in world conflict?

9. How does parenting change from one generation to the next? Compare Lillian and Andy to Rosanna, and Arthur and Frank to Walter. And what about the roles of the sexes?

10. By the end of *Some Luck*, Henry is just becoming an adult and Claire is still a child. What do you think might be ahead for them in the next book(s) of this trilogy?

11. Did your knowledge that *Some Luck* is the first of a trilogy affect your reading of the novel? In what ways is the conclusion of the book definitive, full circle, and in what ways does it leave things open-ended?

STATION ELEVEN
Emily St. John Mandel

A National Book Award Finalist
A PEN/Faulkner Award Finalist
Arthur C. Clarke Award Winner
A Nationwide Best Book of the Year: *The Washington Post, San Francisco Chronicle, Chicago Tribune, Buzzfeed, Entertainment Weekly, Time, Milwaukee Journal Sentinel, The Huffington Post, Time Out, BookRiot*

An audacious, darkly glittering novel about art, fame, and ambition set in the eerie days of civilization's collapse, from the author of three highly acclaimed previous novels.

One snowy night a famous Hollywood actor slumps over and dies onstage during a production of King Lear. Hours later, the world as we know it begins to dissolve. Moving back and forth in time—from the actor's early days as a film star to fifteen years in the future, when a theater troupe known as the Traveling Symphony roams the wasteland of what remains—this suspenseful, elegiac, spellbinding novel charts the strange twists of fate that connect five people: the actor, the man who tried to save him, the actor's first wife, his oldest friend, and a young actress with the Traveling Symphony, caught in the crosshairs of a dangerous self-proclaimed prophet. Sometimes terrifying, sometimes tender, *Station Eleven* tells a story about the relationships that sustain us, the ephemeral nature of fame, and the beauty of the world as we know it.

"Station Eleven *is so compelling, so fearlessly imagined, that I wouldn't have put it down for anything.*" —**Ann Patchett**

"*A superb novel . . . [that] leaves us not fearful for the end of the word but appreciative of the grace of everyday existence.*" —***San Francisco Chronicle***

ABOUT THE AUTHOR: **Emily St. John Mandel** was born in British Columbia, Canada. She is the author of three previous novels—*Last Night in Montreal, The Singer's Gun,* and *The Lola Quartet*—all of which were Indie Next picks. She is a staff writer for *The Millions,* and her work has appeared in numerous anthologies, including The Best American Mystery Stories 2013 and Venice Noir. She lives in New York City with her husband.

June 2015 | Trade Paperback | Fiction | 352 pp | $15.95 | ISBN 9780804172448
Vintage | penguinrandomhouse.com | emilymandel.com

CONVERSATION STARTERS

1. Now that you've read the entire novel, go back and reread the passage by Czeslaw Milosz that serves as an epigraph. What does it mean? Why did Mandel choose it to introduce *Station Eleven*?

2. Does the novel have a main character? Who would you consider it to be?

3. Arthur Leander dies while performing *King Lear*, and the Traveling Symphony performs Shakespeare's works. On page 57, Mandel writes, "Shakespeare was the third born to his parents, but the first to survive infancy. Four of his siblings died young. His son, Hamnet, died at eleven and left behind a twin. Plague closed the theaters again and again, death flickering over the landscape." How do Shakespearean motifs coincide with those of *Station Eleven*, both the novel and the comic?

4. "Survival is insufficient," a line from *Star Trek: Voyager*, is the Traveling Symphony's motto. What does it mean to them?

5. On a related note, some characters—like Clark—believe in preserving and teaching about the time before the flu. But in Kirsten's interview with François Diallo, we learn that there are entire towns that prefer not to: "We went to a place once where the children didn't know the world had ever been different . . . " What are the benefits of remembering, and of not remembering?

6. What do you think happened during the year Kirsten can't remember?

7. Arthur remembers Miranda saying "I regret nothing," and uses that to deepen his understanding of Lear, "a man who regrets everything," as well as his own life. How do his regrets fit into the larger scope of the novel? Other than Miranda, are there other characters that refuse to regret?

8. Throughout the novel, those who were alive during the time before the flu remember specific things about those days: the ease of electricity, the taste of an orange. In their place, what do you think you'd remember most?

9. What do you imagine the Traveling Symphony will find when they reach the brightly lit town to the south?

10. The novel ends with Clark, remembering the dinner party and imagining that somewhere in the world, ships are sailing. Why did Mandel choose to end the novel with him?

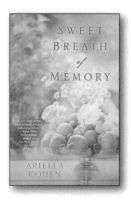

SWEET BREATH OF MEMORY
Ariella Cohen

With its tree-lined streets and curbside planters brimming with spring bulbs, Amberley, Massachusetts seems a good place for Cate Saunders to start over. It's been two years since her husband, John, was killed in Iraq, and life has become something to simply struggle through. Cate's new job as a caregiver doesn't pay much, but the locals are welcoming. Cate's barely unpacked before she's drawn—reluctantly at first—into a circle of friends.

There's Gaby, who nourishes her diner customers' spirits as well as their bodies; feisty Beatrice, who kept the town going when its men marched off to WWII; and Sheila, whose Italian grocery is the soul of the place. Their lives have also been touched by heartache. Soon, within the pages of an old journal found in her apartment, Cate encounters another kindred spirit—a Polish ghetto survivor who also made a new beginning in Amberley. When revelations about Cate's husband's death threaten her newfound peace of mind, these sisters-in-arms' stories will show her an unexpected way forward.

Cate will discover how although we suffer alone, we heal together—learning to balance treasured memories with new dreams.

"Filled with compassion, humor and honesty, Sweet Breath of Memory *is a powerful story of forgiveness. Through food and friendship, a community releases its long held secrets."* —**Karen Brown, author of** ***The Longings of Wayward Girls***

"Ariella Cohen spins a tender yarn about the enduring nature of love, the importance of friendship and the eternal longing for a place to call home. A big hearted story; every page brims with warmth, wisdom and compassion." —**Yona Zeldis McDonough, author of** ***You Were Meant for Me***

About the Author: **Ariella Cohen** is a graduate of Barnard College, the Hebrew University and the University of Michigan Law School. Her short fiction appears in *A Cup of Comfort for Couples*, *Heartscapes*, and *Flashshot*. She lives in New England; visit her at ariellacohenauthor.wordpress.com.

July 2016 | Trade Paperback | Fiction | 400 pp | $15.00 | ISBN 9781496703705
Kensington | kensingtonbooks.com | ariellacohenauthor.wordpress.com

CONVERSATION STARTERS

1. Cate's memories of John are fluid, shifting in and out of focus and becoming abraded by time. She questions if this means her love was somehow flawed. Why do you think some memories remain crisp, while others blur and seem to dim?

2. Cate speaks of memories as a shield against loneliness and despair. Like armor, they're 'initially so shiny they dazzle and in time acquiring the patina of use.' Do you agree? Are there particular memories that have been your armor in life?

3. How does the life path of Cate mirror that of Miriam Rosen? Can the guilt Cate feels over John's death be compared with a Holocaust survivor's guilt?

4. Gaby does not initially tell her closest friends that she is ill. Knowing how her parents' death shadows her life, do you think denying herself the comfort of friendship is a form of self-punishment?

5. Working as a home care aid, Cate wears the uniform of one valued more for what her hands can do than what her mind can imagine. Compare her initial attitude toward caregiving with Gaby's toward waitressing. Both women come to view such manual labor as a form of atonement. Is this healthy?

6. When Helen describes growing up with her mother, the anger and resentment she felt toward Charlotte is obvious even though it was tempered by great love. How can we help friends and colleagues face the unique challenges of caregiving?

7. Who do you think gave Cate Miriam's journal entries? Why were they given to her?

8. At the end of the novel, Cate comes home to Amberley. Compare that scene with her arrival by bus in chapter one. Think about how the women of Amberley changed in the interim. Is Cate a catalyst for change much as Miriam was decades before?

'TIL THE WELL RUNS DRY

Lauren Francis-Sharma

'Til the Well Runs Dry opens in a seaside village in the north of Trinidad where young Marcia Garcia, a gifted and smart-mouthed 16-year-old seamstress, lives alone, raising two small boys and guarding a family secret. When she meets Farouk, an ambitious young policeman, the risks and rewards in Marcia's life amplify forever.

On an island rich with laughter, Calypso, Carnival, cricket, beaches and salty air, sweet fruits and spicy stews, the novel follows Marcia and Farouk from their amusing and passionate courtship through personal and historical events that threaten Marcia's secret, entangle the couple and their children in a scandal, and endanger the future for all of them.

'Til the Well Runs Dry tells the twinned stories of a spirited woman's love for one man and her bottomless devotion to her children. For readers who cherish the previously untold stories of women's lives, here is a story of grit and imperfection and love that has not been told before.

*"Marcia's story, told lovingly in this, Francis-Sharma's debut novel, is as universally touching as it is original." —**The New York Times***

*"You'll hear the calypso music in this vivid debut about a spirited seamstress and devoted mother with a family secret." —**People***

*"'Til the Well Runs Dry burns through its telling like the best gossip, but has the controlled mystery of a fairytale. This narrative is surprising, winding and always gratifying." —**Tiphanie Yanique, author of Land of Love and Drowning***

ABOUT THE AUTHOR: **Lauren Francis-Sharma,** a child of Trinidadian immigrants, was born in New York City and raised in Baltimore, Maryland. She holds a bachelor's degree in English literature with a minor in African-American Studies from the University of Pennsylvania and a J.D. from the University of Michigan Law School. She lives in the Washington, D.C., area with her husband and two children. *'Til the Well Runs Dry* is her first novel.

September 2015 | Trade Paperback | Fiction | 416 pp | $16.00 | ISBN 9781250074676
Picador | us.macmillan.com | laurenfrancissharma.com

CONVERSATION STARTERS

1. Each chapter in *'Til the Well Runs Dry* is told from the perspective of one of three characters. Why do you think the author chose these three characters to tell the story, rather than picking one protagonist? How do you think this choice enhanced the storytelling?

2. Why do you think Marcia chose to keep the story of the twin brothers a secret from Farouk, knowing that some version of the story could get back to Farouk sooner or later?

3. Why do you think, out of all of her children, Marcia was the hardest on Jacqueline?

4. Freedom vs. commitment are large themes in this book. How does a desire for freedom inform each character's story? What role does commitment play in limiting their desire for freedom?

5. Farouk wanted badly to take Marcia away from Blanchisseuse, yet close to the end of the novel he packed up all his children and took a day trip there. Why was it so important for him to go back?

6. What do you think was the reason behind Patsy's rebellion?

7. When Jacqueline left home, the Garcia house went to shambles. Earlier in the story, Marcia had taken pride in keeping a clean house; what does the messy home symbolize?

8. Inspector Chung Marlock told Marcia that she was the kind of woman "who's always looking to find a way out." Do you think this was true? What impact do these words have on Marcia?

9. For Marcia, New York symbolized risk. How did going to New York change her? Were you shocked when she went to visit Mrs. Silverman's a second time? Why or why not?

10. Were you surprised when you found out about the brothers? How do you think Marcia's life would have been different if they weren't taken away from her?

11. This novel sheds light on many of the challenges immigrants face in America. Why, after all the mistreatment she suffered, does Marcia still feel as if bringing her children to America is the right decision?

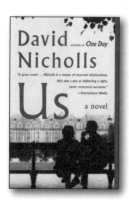

US
David Nicholls

Douglas Petersen may be mild mannered, but behind his reserve lies a sense of humor that, against all odds, seduces beautiful Connie into a second date . . . and eventually into marriage. Now, almost three decades after their relationship first blossomed in London, they live more or less happily in the suburbs with their moody seventeen-year-old son, Albie.

Then Connie tells Douglas that she thinks she wants a divorce.

The timing couldn't be worse. Hoping to encourage her son's artistic interests, Connie has planned a monthlong tour of European capitals, a chance to experience the world's greatest works of art as a family, and she can't bring herself to cancel. Douglas is privately convinced that this landmark trip will rekindle the romance in the marriage, and may even help him to bond with Albie.

From the streets of Amsterdam to the famed museums of Paris, from the cafés of Venice to the beaches of Barcelona, Douglas's odyssey brings Europe to vivid life just as he experiences a powerful awakening of his own. Will this summer be his last as a husband, or the moment when he turns his marriage, and maybe even his whole life, around?

"I loved this book. Funny, sad, tender: for anyone who wants to know what happens after the Happy Ever After." —**Jojo Moyes, author of *Me Before You and One Plus One***

"A great novel...Nicholls is a master of nuanced relationships." —***Entertainment Weekly***

About the Author: **David Nicholls**'s most recent novel, the *New York Times* bestseller *One Day*, has sold more than two million copies and has been translated into thirty-seven languages; the film adaptation starred Jim Sturgess and Anne Hathaway. Nicholls's previous novels include *Starter for Ten* and *The Understudy*. He trained as an actor before making the switch to writing and has twice been nominated for BAFTA awards.

June 2015 | Trade Paperback | Fiction | 416 pp | $15.99 | ISBN 9780062365590
Harper Paperbacks | harpercollins.com | davidnichollswriter.com

CONVERSATION STARTERS

1. Describe Douglas, Connie and Albie and their family dynamic. What draws Douglas and Connie together? What drives them apart? How has their marriage evolved over the years and how does it affect their family life and their son?

2. This novel is about marriage—not just a boy-meets-girl romance. What does the author tell us about the Happily Ever After part? How does "real life" compare with our romanticized notions? Do spouses have a responsibility to keep the spark alive after the honeymoon stage?

3. How important is it for a person to stay true to their individuality? How do we reconcile individuality within relationships and families?

4. Travel is a major component of this novel. How does being physically away from home affect the characters? What opportunities does traveling offer them? What emotional challenges does it raise?

5. How does Douglas cope when his "Grand Tour" plans aren't working out? How does he adjust over the course of his journey?

6. The parent-child relationship can be as frustrating as it is rewarding. What are the particular sources of turmoil in the relationship between Douglas and Albie? What helps them resolve their differences?

7. How does an instant-gratification culture affect our ability to work through tough times? Do people give up on relationships too easily? What about Douglas and Connie? What about Albie?

8. The meaning of love can change over the course of a relationship. Describe Douglas' love for Connie and Albie. Compare and contrast the novel's beginning to its end. How have the characters changed? Stayed the same? What have they learned?

9. Each section begins with a quote. What do the quotes add to each section? What do they add to the story as a whole? Which quote struck you the most? Why?

10. Between the "Grand Tour," Connie's painting and Albie's photography, art is at the very center of *Us*. How does art affect the characters? How does art affect our lives?

11. The novel is called *Us*. Is there really an "Us" in the story? If yes, who? If no, what inspired the title?

A VIEW OF THE HARBOUR

Elizabeth Taylor
Introduction by Roxana Robinson

Self-deception and betrayal are Elizabeth Taylor's great subjects, and in *A View of the Harbour* she turns her unsparing gaze on the emotional and sexual politics of a seedy seaside town that's been left behind by modernity. Tory, recently divorced, depends more and more on the company of her neighbors Robert, a doctor, and Beth, a busy author of melodramatic novels. Prudence, Robert and Beth's daughter, disapproves of the intimacy that has grown between her parents and Tory and the gossip it has awakened in their little community. As the novel proceeds, Taylor's view widens to take in a range of characters from bawdy, nosey Mrs. Bracey; to a widowed young proprietor of the local waxworks, Lily Wilson; to the would-be artist Bertram—while the book as a whole offers a beautifully observed and written examination of the fictions around which we construct our lives and manage our losses.

"*A View of the Harbour may be Taylor's most nuanced study of the push and pull between domestic and artistic labor.*" —**Namara Smith, The New Yorker**

"*Jane Austen, Elizabeth Taylor, Barbara Pym, Elizabeth Bowen—soul sisters all.*" —**Anne Tyler**

ABOUT THE AUTHOR: **Elizabeth Taylor** (1912–1975) was a short-story writer and novelist. Her first novel, *At Mrs. Lippincote's*, came out in 1945. She would go on to publish eleven more novels, including *Angel* and *A Game of Hide and Seek* (both available from NYRB Classics). In 2014, NYRB published *You'll Enjoy It When You Get There*, a selection made by Margaret Drabble of Taylor's short stories, many of which first appeared in *The New Yorker*.

Roxana Robinson is the author of eight works of fiction, including the novels *Cost* and *Sparta*. She is also the author of *Georgia O'Keeffe: A Life*. A Guggenheim fellow, she edited *The New York Stories of Edith Wharton*, published by NYRB Classics in 2007.

June 2015 | Trade Paperback | Fiction | 320 pp | $16.95 | ISBN 9781590178485
NYRB Classics | nybooks.com

CONVERSATION STARTERS

1. How do Elizabeth Taylor's descriptions of characters watching the harbor town through windows mirror the way in which Taylor structures and narrates the novel?

2. Bertram and Beth are both artists—one a painter, the other a writer. In what ways do their attitudes toward their work and "the life of an artist" differ?

3. *A View of the Harbour* is set in the years following World War II. Did you feel that the post-war setting affected the mood of the novel?

4. Where in the novel did you find Taylor's use of irony most effective?

5. On page 186, Beth contemplates the responsibilities of women versus the duties of men. "'A man,' she thought suddenly, 'would consider this a business outing. But then, a man would not have to cook the meals for the day overnight, nor consign his child to a friend, nor leave half-done the ironing, nor forget the grocery orders as I now discover I have forgotten it. The artfulness of men,' she thought. 'They implant in us, foster in us, instincts to which, in the end, we feel the shame of not possessing'" (186). Does the above quote (and the novel as a whole) give you a sense of the author's thoughts on art vs. domestic life? Is there any character in the book who seems to succeed at both?

6. In the introduction to *A View of the Harbour*, Roxana Robinson writes, "A quietly subversive strain runs throughout [Taylor's] work." In what ways did you find the novel subversive?

7. Do you find Robert to be a sympathetic character? Did he become more or less so because of the way he handles the affair with Tory?

8. How does the harbor town itself act as a character in the book?

9. Prudence, often described as "poor Prudence," is stuck between school, and finding work and marriage. To what degree do you think Prudence's condition is influenced by her family, the time period in which she lives, and her own personality?

10. What were your impressions of Tory? Did you sympathize with her at any points in the novel? In what ways does Taylor make Tory a complicated character? Did you find the return of her ex-husband, Teddy, to be a satisfying end to the novel?

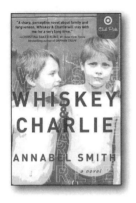

WHISKEY & CHARLIE
Annabel Smith

Whiskey and Charlie might have come from the same family, but they'd tell you two completely different stories about growing up. Whiskey is everything Charlie is not—bold, daring, carefree—and Charlie blames his twin brother for always stealing the limelight, always getting everything, always pushing Charlie back.

When they were just boys, the secret language they whispered back and forth over their crackly walkie-talkies connected them, in a way. The two-way alphabet (alpha, bravo, charlie, delta) became their code, their lifeline. But as the brothers grew up, they grew apart. By the time the twins reach adulthood, they are barely even speaking to each other.

When Charlie hears that Whiskey has been in a terrible accident and has slipped into a coma, Charlie can't make sense of it. Who is he without Whiskey? As days and weeks slip by and the chances of Whiskey recovering grow ever more slim, Charlie is forced to consider that he may never get to say all the things he wants to say. A compelling and unforgettable novel about rivalry and redemption, *Whiskey & Charlie* is perfect for anyone whose family has ever been less than picture-perfect.

"A sharp, perceptive novel about family and forgiveness, Whiskey & Charlie will stay with me for a very long time."—**Christina Baker Kline, #1 New York Times bestselling author of Orphan Train**

"A finely crafted novel that keeps us reading because we care about the characters. It's a terrific book."—**Graeme Simsion, New York Times bestselling author of The Rosie Project and The Rosie Effect**

About the Author: **Annabel Smith** has been a writer-in-residence at Katherine Susannah Prichard Writers Centre and the Fellowship of Australian Writers. In 2012 she was selected as one of five inaugural recipients of the Creative Australia Fellowship for Emerging Artists. She lives in Perth, Australia, with her husband and son.

April 2015 | Trade Paperback | Fiction | 336 pp | $14.99 | ISBN 9781492607861
Sourcebooks | sourcebooks.com | annabelsmith.com

CONVERSATION STARTERS

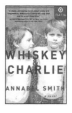

1. *Whiskey & Charlie* is structured around the two-way alphabet. How does the author use the two-way alphabet as a narrative device within the story?

2. What are Charlie's perceptions of his brother, and how do they change over the course of the novel?

3. Do you relate to Charlie's feelings about Whiskey? Have you had a time where you felt resentful or jealous of a sibling? How did you resolve those feelings?

4. In what ways does Whiskey's accident force Charlie to grow up? Is there a defining moment in Charlie's maturation?

5. How has Whiskey's accident affected the other members of their family?

6. Suppose that Charlie had been the one in a coma rather than Whiskey. How do you think Whiskey would have handled that situation? What are some regrets he may have had about their relationship?

7. Charlie loves Juliet yet is afraid to marry her. What stops Charlie from proposing to Juliet or from accepting her proposal? And what finally makes him change his mind?

8. How does the counseling Charlie receives in the hospital help him to resolve the issues in his life? How might things have worked out differently if he had received that kind of help earlier?

9. How does Charlie's relationship with Whiskey affect his relationships with others around him, including his mother, his father, and Juliet?

10. What role does Rosa play in the novel, as a relative newcomer to the family and in the dynamic between Whiskey and Charlie?

11. What role do you think Mike plays in the story? How does his arrival further complicate Charlie's feelings about Whiskey?

12. For most of the novel, it is unknown whether Whiskey will recover from his accident. What are some issues related to quality of life and euthanasia that arise in this story?

13. Does *Whiskey & Charlie* have a happy ending?

THE WINTER PEOPLE
Jennifer McMahon

A Boston Globe Best Book of the Year

A simmering literary thriller of the unbreakable bonds between mothers and their children, *The Winter People* showcases the spellbinding talent that has made Jennifer McMahon a bestselling storyteller. This tale of ghostly secrets and dark choices takes us to rural West Hall, Vermont, a town known for strange disappearances. The most legendary victim is Sara Harrison Shea. In 1908, she was found dead in the field behind her house just months after the tragic death of her daughter, Gertie. More than a century later, Sara's farmhouse is inhabited by a family that savors the simple life, existing off the grid and practicing sustainable farming. When their mother suddenly vanishes without a trace, it's up to nineteen-year-old daughter Ruthie to track her down. Desperate for clues, she discovers Sara's diary hidden in her mother's bedroom, opening Ruthie's eyes to a world of "sleeper" souls—and the desperate mourners who dare to wake them.

"One of the year's most chilling novels. . . . Enthralling."
—The Miami Herald

"Crisp, mysterious and scary. . . . Reminiscent of Stephen King."
—USA Today

"A hauntingly beautiful read." **—Oprah.com**

About the Author: **Jennifer McMahon** is the author of six novels, including the *New York Times* bestsellers *Island of Lost Girls* and *Promise Not to Tell*. She graduated from Goddard College and studied poetry in the MFA Writing Program at Vermont College. She currently lives with her partner and daughter in Montpelier, Vermont.

January 2015 | Trade Paperback | Fiction | 400 pp | $14.95 | ISBN 9780804169967
Anchor | penguinrandomhouse.com | jennifer-mcmahon.com

CONVERSATION STARTERS

1. At the heart of the novel is the longing to be reunited with a loved one who has died. How would you respond to this possibility, even if you could only see your beloved for one week? What risks would you take to take to experience such a reunion?

2. What was it like to read Sara's diary, alternating with scenes from other time periods? Did Sara's words change your vision of the spirit world? Did her bond with Gertie remind you of your own experience with a mother's love?

3. When Alice and her family inhabit Sara's house and her land, how does that environment transform them? Do you believe that the history of a locale can influence your present-day experiences there?

4. Ruthie and Fawn have been raised to question authority and to live a non-materialistic life. What benefits and challenges does their upbringing give them when their mother goes missing? Ultimately, what did Alice try to teach her daughters about becoming fulfilled women?

5. Martin cherishes Sara and continually strives to please her. Does she love him in equal measure, or does her ancestry make it too difficult for an outsider to fully share a life with her?

6. How was Sara affected by her history with her siblings, Constance and Jacob? Why did their father easily become dependent on Auntie, while Sara's mother didn't trust her?

7. How did you react to Gertie's hunger? What is its significance to the maternal women who must care for her?

8. Consider the rules for waking a sleeper. What do the words and the ingredients represent in terms of the cycles of life and the nature of death?

9. What were your theories about the many unsolved deaths in West Hall? Did your instincts prove to be correct when the truth about the Devil's Hand was revealed?

10. In *The Winter People* and previous novels by Jennifer McMahon that you have enjoyed, how is the author able to make surreal situations seem highly realistic? What role do fear and courage play in each of her books?

WOLF WINTER
Cecilia Ekbäck

Swedish Lapland, 1717 – Maija, her husband Paavo and her daughters Frederika and Dorotea arrive from their native Finland, hoping to forget the traumas of their past and put down new roots in this harsh but beautiful land. Above them looms Blackåsen, a mountain whose foreboding presence looms over the valley and whose dark history seems to haunt the lives of those who live in its shadow. One day, Frederika happens upon the mutilated body of one of their neighbors. The death is dismissed as a wolf attack, but Maija feels certain that the wounds could only have been inflicted by another man. She's compelled to investigate, determined to find answers for herself—just as the "wolf winter," the harshest winter in memory, descends upon the settlers, threatening her family's survival. Chilling both in landscape and plot, Cecilia Ekbäck's debut novel is a remarkable work of sophisticated suspense and beautiful prose.

"The time and place seem so remote as to be unearthly, and the style has a stealthy quality, like a silent fall of snow; suddenly, the reader is enveloped. Visually acute, skillfully written; it won't easily erase its tracks in the reader's mind." —**Hilary Mantel, Man Booker Prize-Winning Author**

"This snapshot of life in a place where winter can be unspeakably cruel, where simply staying alive is a victory, proves irresistible." —*The Kirkus Review*

"Exquisitely suspenseful, beautifully written, and highly recommended." —**Lee Child, #1 International Bestselling Author**

"A compelling, suspenseful story." —*Sunday Times*

ABOUT THE AUTHOR: **Cecilia Ekbäck** was born in Sweden in a small northern town. Her parents come from Lapland. In Wolf Winter, her first novel, she returns home to the landscape and the characters of her childhood. Ekbäck is a Professional Member of PEN American Center. She lives in Calgary with her husband and twin daughters.

January 2015 | Hardcover | Fiction | 376 pp | $26.00 | ISBN 9781602862524
November 2015 | Trade Paperback | Fiction | 376 pp | $16.00 | ISBN 9781602862944
Weinstein Books | weinsteinbooks.com | ceciliaekback.com

CONVERSATION STARTERS

1. To what extent does landscape affect the behavior of the characters in *Wolf Winter*?

2. There are three narrators in this story: Maija, Frederika, and the priest. How do their narrative styles differ?

3. Women are at the center of this story. Given the period in which the book is set, their agency is limited. How easy is it for a modern reader to accept this?

4. How would you characterize the relationship between Maija and Frederika?

5. Jutta, Majia's grandmother, appears to her. What role does she play?

6. Why is Maija so hostile to Frederika's gifts?

7. What role do animals – real and imagined – play in this story?

8. Other, older belief systems lie very close to the surface of people's lives on Blackåsen Mountain. How does the Church attempt to control and manipulate them for its own end?

9. Cecila Ekbäck has described a 'Wolf Winter' as a moment in our lives when we confront our very darkest thoughts. How do the three main characters emerge from their Wolf Winters?

10. What do you imagine lies in store for the priest?

11. When Maija's husband returns (we may assume he does), how might their relationship have changed?

12. Each of the settlers has brought with them to their new homes on Blackåsen Mountain the burdens of their pasts. How do the events in the book impact on them?

13. What lies behind Elin Eriksson's actions?

14. The Lapps lead their lives largely in parallel to the settlers. What happens when the two communities come together?

15. Why does Maija persist in her inquiries?

16. Do you think the priest is a moral, immoral, or amoral agent in the story?

17. Why do you think the other settlers regard Maija as a threat?

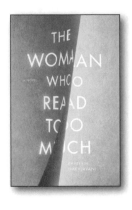

THE WOMAN WHO TOO MUCH
Bahiyyih Nakhjavani

Gossip was rife in the capital about the poetess of Qazvin. Some claimed she had been arrested for masterminding the murder of the grand Mullah, her uncle. Others echoed her words, and passed her poems from hand to hand. Everyone spoke of her beauty, and her dazzling intelligence. But most alarming to the Shah and the court was how the poetess could read. As her warnings and predictions became prophecies fulfilled, about the assassination of the Shah, the hanging of the Mayor, and the murder of the Grand Vazir, many wondered whether she was not only reading history but writing it as well. Was she herself guilty of the crimes she was foretelling?

Set in the world of the Qajar monarchs, mayors, ministers, and mullahs, this book explores the dangerous and at the same time luminous legacy left by a remarkable person. Bahiyyih Nakhjavani offers a gripping tale that is at once a compelling history of a pioneering woman, a story of nineteenth century Iran told from the street level up, and a work that is universally relevant to our times.

"Nakhjavani displays a love of storytelling almost for its own sake."
—Literary Review

*"Bahiyyih Nakhjavani is best—really very effective—when she writes of the sandstorms and delusions of our own imperfect Earth." —**The Washington Post***

*"One of the year's 10 best books to lose yourself in . . . Nakhjavani deftly transforms an incomplete history into legend. An ambitious effort produces an expertly crafted epic." —**Kirkus Reviews***

*"Nakhjavani's anachronistic style sets the novel apart from the bulk of contemporary literary fiction and adds immensely to its charm." —**Publishers Weekly***

ABOUT THE AUTHOR: **Bahiyyih Nakhjavani** grew up in Uganda, was educated in the United Kingdom and the United States, and now lives in France. Her novels have been published in French, Italian, Spanish, German, Dutch, Greek, Turkish, Hebrew, Russian, and Korean.

March 2015 | Hardcover | Fiction | 336 pp | $24.00 | ISBN 9780804793254
Redwood Press | sup.org

CONVERSATION STARTERS

1. What was the poetess's crime? Challenging authority? Going against established gender roles? Or do you think she even committed a crime?

2. How does the "love" of the Mother for her son, the Shah, compare to the "love" of the father for the poetess of Qazvin? How do their relationships compare to the relationship between the poetess of Qazvin and her daughter?

3. Many characters find themselves confined: the Mother in the *anderoun*, the poetess in the Mayor's house, the Shah in the mausoleum, the Vazir in the bathhouse. For the women, they still exercise power from their confinement. For the men, they often end up dead. What does this show about the sources of power and influence? Does this affect women and men differently?

4. Did you find the character of the corpse washer appealing or menacing? Or both? How does her character evolve throughout the story?

5. The British Envoy's wife is one of three literate women. How does her life compare to the poetess of Qazvin's? Do they write for the same reasons? The Envoy's wife is "Western" – what does that imply?

6. In what ways do silence, speech, and rumor shape the way the narrative progresses? Who keeps secrets? Who lies? What are their motivations? Is writing a form of "speech" or "silence"?

7. How is food woven into the storyline? In what ways does it affect the action?

8. How does the sequence that the events are revealed affect the way you perceived the characters? Does the author risk confusing the reader? If so, do you think it's worth the risk?

9. In today's news, we continue to hear stories about Muslim women and veiling, and gender roles and expectations in the East and West. What contemporary parallels do you see in the story of the poetess?

NONFICTION

BEING MORTAL
Medicine and What Matters in the End
Atul Gawande

In *Being Mortal*, bestselling author Atul Gawande tackles the hardest challenge of his profession: how medicine can not only improve life but also the process of its ending

Medicine has triumphed in modern times, transforming birth, injury, and infectious disease from harrowing to manageable. But in the inevitable condition of aging and death, the goals of medicine seem too frequently to run counter to the interest of the human spirit. Nursing homes, preoccupied with safety, pin patients into railed beds and wheelchairs. Hospitals isolate the dying, checking for vital signs long after the goals of cure have become moot. Doctors, committed to extending life, continue to carry out devastating procedures that in the end extend suffering.

Gawande, a practicing surgeon, addresses his profession's ultimate limitation, arguing that quality of life is the desired goal for patients and families. Gawande offers examples of freer, more socially fulfilling models for assisting the infirm and dependent elderly, and he explores the varieties of hospice care to demonstrate that a person's last weeks or months may be rich and dignified.

Full of eye-opening research and riveting storytelling, *Being Mortal* asserts that medicine can comfort and enhance our experience even to the end, providing not only a good life but also a good end.

"Being Mortal is not only wise and deeply moving, it is an essential and insightful book for our times, as one would expect from Atul Gawande, one of our finest physician writers." —**Oliver Sacks**

ABOUT THE AUTHOR: **Atul Gawande** is author of three bestselling books: *Complications*, *Better*, and *The Checklist Manifesto*. He is also a surgeon at Brigham and Women's Hospital in Boston, a staff writer for *The New Yorker*, and a professor at Harvard Medical School and the Harvard School of Public Health. He and his wife have three children and live in Newton, Massachusetts.

October 2014 | Hardcover | Nonfiction | 304 pp | $26.00 | ISBN 9780805095159
April 2016 | Trade Paperback | Nonfiction | 304 pp | $16.00 | ISBN 9781250076229
Metropolitan Books | henryholt.com | atulgawande.com

CONVERSATION STARTERS

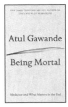

1. Why do we assume we will know how to empathize and comfort those in end-of-life stages? How prepared do you feel to do and say the right thing when that time comes for someone in your life?

2. What do you think the author means when he says that we've "medicalized mortality"? How does *The Death of Ivan Ilyich* illustrate the suffering that can result? Have you ever witnessed such suffering?

3. As a child, what did you observe about the aging process? How was mortality discussed in your family?

4. Did you read Alice Hobson's story as an inspiring one, or as a cautionary tale?

5. Do you know couples like Felix and Bella? The last days for Bella were so hard on Felix, but do you think he'd have had it any other way? Was there anything more others could have done for this couple?

6. What realities are captured in the story of Lou Sanders and his daughter, Shelley, regarding home care? What conflicts did Shelley face between her intentions and the practical needs of the family and herself? What does the book illustrate about the universal nature of this struggle in families around the globe?

7. The author writes, "It is not death that the very old tell me they fear. It is what happens short of death…" (55). What do you fear most about the end of life? How do you think your family would react if you told them, "I'm ready"? How do we strike a balance between fear and hope, while still confronting reality?

8. Often medical treatments do not work. Yet our society seems to favor attempts to "fix" health problems, no matter the odds of their success. Dr. Gawande quotes statistics that show 25% of Medicare spending goes to the 5% of patients in the last stages of life. Why do you think it's so difficult for doctors and/or families to refuse or curtail treatment? How should priorities be set?

9. How was your reading affected by the book's final scene, as Dr. Gawande fulfills his father's wishes? How do tradition and spirituality influence your concept of what it means to be mortal?

CAN'T WE TALK ABOUT SOMETHING MORE PLEASANT?
A Memoir
Roz Chast

Through words and illustrations, with evident pain and remarkable humor, Roz Chast revisits the struggle she went through with her aging parents as their physical and mental abilities gradually declined and they eventually became unable to care for themselves.

"This extraordinarily honest, searing and hilarious graphic memoir captures (and helps relieve) the unbelievable stress that results when the tables turn and grown children are left taking care of their parents." —**San Francisco Chronicle**

"Gut-wrenching and laugh-aloud funny. I want to recommend it to everyone I know who has elderly parents, or might have them someday." —**Milwaukee Journal Sentinel**

"One of the great autobiographical memoirs of our time." —**Buffalo News**

ABOUT THE AUTHOR: **Roz Chast** grew up in Brooklyn. She has been a cartoonist for the New Yorker since 1978, and has written and illustrated several books. *Can't We Talk About Something More Pleasant?* won the 2014 National Book Critics Circle Award, the 2014 Kirkus Prize in nonfiction, and was a finalist for the National Book Award. It was also named one of the Best Books of 2014 by more than fifty media outlets, including *People*, Oprah.com, and National Public Radio.

May 2014 | Hardcover | Nonfiction | 240 pp | $28.00 | ISBN 9781608198061
Bloomsbury USA | bloomsbury.com | rozchast.com

CONVERSATION STARTERS

1. Have you had a similar discussion with your parents and/or children about aging and long-term care plans? What was the result? At what age do you think parents and children should have this conversation?

2. Which part(s) of the book, if any, could you relate to the most? Did you find yourself empathizing more with George and Elizabeth, or Roz? Did this change as you progressed through the book?

3. Which aspects of the role reversal Chast depicts—the child assuming a caretaker role—were the most striking to you? What emotions did you experience as you were reading about the challenges Roz, George, and Elizabeth all faced?

4. Did you enjoy Chast's technique of telling her story through illustrations? Why or why not? Were there scenes in the book that you thought were more or less effective because they were depicted in cartoons rather than in straightforward text? Which ones, and why?

5. Whose experience is more frightening to you—George and Elizabeth's, or Roz's?

6. Which parts of the memoir made you laugh? Which made you cry? Did Chast's use of humor surprise you? Do you think it's necessary or inappropriate to approach this type of subject with humor?

7. In the chapter "The Fall," would you have done anything differently than Roz did? Who did you sympathize with the most in this section?

8. Did your perceptions of George and Elizabeth as parents, spouses, and people in general change as the book went on? If so, in what ways?

9. Were there scenes in the book that you found exasperating? If so, which ones and why?

10. What do you think George and Elizabeth would think about the ways in which they're represented in the memoir?

11. In your opinion, what is the greatest loss that George and Elizabeth experience as they age?

12. Have you considered your own end-of-life plans? Why or why not? Was the book informational for you, and if so, what did you learn? Has reading this book changed your thinking about your own end-of-life care?

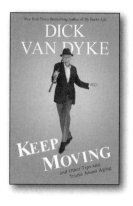

KEEP MOVING
And Other Tips and Truths about Aging
Dick Van Dyke

Hollywood icon Dick Van Dyke will celebrate his 90th birthday in December 2015. He is a beloved legend, having starred in *Mary Poppins*, *Chitty Chitty Bang Bang*, and *The Dick Van Dyke Show*. And he is still keeping himself busy, entertaining America on television, movies, the stage, and social media. Everyone wonders, "How does he do it?" For the first time, Van Dyke will share his secrets and tips on aging: Just keep moving.

Keep Moving is a heartwarming memoir and inspiring instruction book on how to embrace aging with a positive attitude. The chapters are filled with exclusive personal anecdotes that explore various themes on aging: how to adapt to the physical and social changes, deal with loss of friends and loved ones, stay current, fall in love again, and "keep moving" every day like there's no tomorrow.

Praise for *My Lucky Life In and Out of Showbusiness*

"Van Dyke tells a wonderful story about himself and his times. And — in an often surprisingly relevant manner — our times. We've always liked the performer — it's hard not to like Dick Van Dyke — but this will make you admire him." —**Playbill**

"In my opinion, 'Luck' has little to do with Dick Van Dyke's life. It is, rather, his innate kindness and talent that have had an extraordinary effect in shaping the man. And what a fascinating self-portrait he's given us in this book." —**Mary Tyler Moore**

ABOUT THE AUTHOR: **Dick Van Dyke** is a Hollywood icon and *New York Times* bestselling author of *My Lucky Life In and Out of Show Business*. He has received the Theatre World Award, a Tony, a Grammy, and four Emmy awards, as well as the Screen Actors Guild Life Achievement Award in 2013. He lives in California.

October 2015 | Hardcover | Fiction | 256 pp | $25.99 | ISBN 9781602862968
Weinstein Books | weinsteinbooks.com

CONVERSATION STARTERS

1. Even though Dick Van Dyke is nearly ninety years old, he says he does not act or even feel old. How do you think a positive outlook can affect your behavior? Do you agree with Dick that there is no need to "act your age"?

2. Dick speaks briefly about how his father was "genetically poised to live a long life," and yet dies at seventy-six. How do you think his father's outlook differed from Dick's? How is his father's death revisited when Dick is fighting for his own life? Which of Dick's other family members influenced him profoundly?

3. Dick has described himself as a "worrier," but in his older years, he says that his worrying has been a "waste of time." Why should older people worry less, in Dick's opinion?

4. Dick and his brother Jerry have both followed similar paths in life, yet Jerry has a more pessimistic attitude towards aging. Consider Jerry's thoughts on the dog Rocky's health. In what way is Jerry's attitude towards Rocky ironic?

5. Dick reveals that he has been asked to perform several times on "Dancing with The Stars." Why does he refuse?

6. Which tips in this book can be adapted universally for healthy aging? Does Dick provide any advice that would benefit only a few?

7. How do you think this book will benefit an aging demographic? Do you think Dick's thoughts and advice on aging will help younger readers prepare for old age?

8. How did the philosophy of "Keep Moving" influence Dick's life following Michelle's death?

9. Dick's lighthearted narrative takes a more serious term when he speaks about his encounters with ageism. Have you seen ageism elsewhere in literature? Has there been a time in your life where you encountered ageism?

10. Having been born in the 1920s, Dick has seen a great deal of history unfold. How does his connection to history influence his conviction that the young should communicate more with the old?

MA, HE SOLD ME FOR A FEW CIGARETTES
A Memoir of Dublin in the 1950s
Martha Long

When young Martha Long's feckless mother hooks up with Jackser ("that bandy aul bastard"), and starts having more babies, the abuse and poverty in the house grow more acute. Martha is regularly sent out to beg and more often steal, and her wiles (as a child of seven or eight) are often the only thing keeping food on the table. Jackser is a master of paranoid anger and outbursts, keeping the children in an unheated tenement, unable to go to school, ready prey to his unpredictable rages. Then Martha is sent by Jackser to a man he knows in exchange for the price of a few cigarettes. She is nine. She is filthy, lice-ridden, outcast. Martha and her Ma escape to England, but, for an itinerant Irishwoman, finding work in late 1950s England is a near impossibility.

Martha treasures the time alone with her mother, but – amazingly – Ma pines for Jackser. They return to the other children and to Dublin, where daily life is an ordeal once again. And yet there are prized cartoon magazines, the occasional hidden penny to buy the children sweets, glimpses of loving family life in other houses, and Martha's hope that she will soon be old enough to make her own way.

"Reading this startling testament to one child's valiant attempts to live until the age of sixteen is a worthy reminder that we can do better as adults if we turn to embrace the children who are suffering, anywhere on earth..."
—**Alice Walker, author of *The Color Purple***

ABOUT THE AUTHOR: **Martha Long** was born in the 1950s in Dublin, Ireland, where she still lives today. A natural-born storyteller with virtually no formal education, she is the author of seven "Ma" books, all of which have been bestsellers in Ireland. She calls herself a "middle-aged matron" and has successfully reared three children.

September 2012 | Trade Paperback | Nonfiction | 496 pp | $16.95 | ISBN 9781609805C
Seven Stories Press | sevenstories.com | marthalong.wordpress.com

CONVERSATION STARTERS

1. Clearly, Sally and Jacker have something short of an ideal relationship. And yet they stay together. Sally even returns from England after escaping to get away from Jackser, and immediately takes up with him again. Why? What is it that, in spite of the many obvious problems in their relationship, keeps the two together?

2. Early in the book, Martha's aunt Nelly and cousin Barney give shelter to Sally and Martha. The arrangement is far from ideal, but in many ways superior to Martha's later life with Jackser. And yet, Nelly and Barney quickly recede into the past and are hardly mentioned later in the book. When they are mentioned, it is quite fondly ("Me heart is jerkin at the thought of them times"). So why do they disappear?

3. One of the book's most heart-stopping scenes comes when Jackser brutalizes Sally and then dangles her infant son over a staircase, threatening to kill him as "another man's leavins." At other times, however, while he is never tender-hearted, Jackser does accept some responsibility for the children and in his own way attempts to help raise them. How does Jackser seem to understand his own role in Martha's family?

4. *Ma, He Sold Me For a Few Cigarettes* is the first book in a series of seven, the first four of which are now available in North America. Based on what we know about young Martha and her world so far, what predictions do you have for Martha's future as it will be described in subsequent volumes?

5. Young Martha is subjected to cruelty beyond what many of us can easily imagine or might be able to handle. And yet Martha, just a girl with little beside her indomitable spirit to prop her up, survives this volume and its six sequels, to become the Martha Long who authored these books. What is it about young Martha that enables her to withstand so much? How does she survive and even thrive amid all the suffering she's endured?

MY GRANDFATHER WOULD HAVE SHOT ME
A Black Woman Discovers Her Family's Nazi Past
Jennifer Teege and Nikola Sellmair

When Jennifer Teege, a German-born black woman, happens to pluck a library book from the shelf, she discovers a horrifying fact: Her grandfather was Amon Goeth, the vicious Nazi concentration camp commandant chillingly depicted by Ralph Fiennes in *Schindler's List*. The more Teege reads about Goeth, the more certain she becomes: If her grandfather had met her—a black woman—he would have killed her. Teege's discovery sends her, at age 38, on a quest to fully comprehend her family's haunted history.

Award-winning journalist Nikola Sellmair contributes an interwoven narrative that draws on original interviews with Teege's family and friends and adds historical context. Ultimately, Teege's resolute search for the truth leads her, step by step, to the possibility of her own liberation.

"Jennifer Teege's new memoir traces the pain of discovering her grandfather was the real-life 'Nazi butcher' from Schindler's List.*"—**People***

*"Haunting and unflinching. . . . A memoir, an adoption story, and a geopolitical history lesson, all blended seamlessly into an account of Teege's exploration of her roots." —**Washington Post***

*"Stunning."—**Booklist**, starred review*

*"Unforgettable."—**Publishers Weekly***

*"A gripping read, highly recommended."—**Library Journal**, starred review*

*"[An] amazing story of horror and reconciliation and love." —**John Mutter, Shelf Awareness***

ABOUT THE AUTHOR: **Jennifer Teege** worked in advertising for 16 years before becoming an author. She lives in Germany with her husband and two sons. **Nikola Sellmair** is a reporter at Germany's *Stern* magazine. She received the German-Polish Journalist Award for the first-ever article about Jennifer Teege's singular story.

April 2015 | Hardcover | Nonfiction | 240 pp | $24.95 | ISBN 9781615192533
April 2016 | Trade Paperback | Nonfiction | 240 pp | $14.95 | ISBN 9781615193080
The Experiment | theexperimentpublishing.com

CONVERSATION STARTERS

1. The *Washington Post* describes this book as equal parts "memoir, adoption story, and geopolitical history lesson." As Jennifer Teege researches and reflects on the Goeth family, Nazism, and her own adoption and childhood, which do you think affects her the most? Which was most interesting to you?

2. The book is presented from intertwined perspectives: Jennifer's first-person and Nikola Sellmair's third-person. Discuss how the two authors complement and complicate one another's views.

3. On crossing the boundary between fiction and history, Jennifer writes, "Slowly I begin to grasp that the Amon Goeth in the film *Schindler's List* is not a fictional character, but a person who actually existed in flesh and blood" (7). How has your view of the Holocaust been shaped by popular culture? Has this book changed your perspective?

4. Jennifer has trouble reconciling her memory of a beloved grandmother with the truth of a woman who lived with Goeth and ignored his atrocities. What does Jennifer's attitude towards Ruth, and Ruth's towards Goeth, suggest about love? Is it possible to love one part of a person while rejecting another?

5. Monika Goeth, named for a father she never met, belongs to the first generation of descendants of Nazi perpetrators. She believes it was "Goeth's story that shaped her identity" (99). How was her experience with the family history different from Jennifer's? How will that experience change for Jennifer's children? Can family trauma be passed down through generations?

6. After living in Israel, Jennifer has strong ties to its culture and people. She feels guilty about her family history and is reluctant to share it with her Israeli friends. Discuss her fears and their reactions. How would you have acted in Jennifer's place, or reacted as her friend?

7. Jennifer describes her skin color as a "barrier" between her and Goeth (41) and as "good camouflage" (175) in Israel. Describing the African quarter of Paris, she says, "I had a sense of homecoming" (184). What role does race play in Jennifer's quest for identity?

ON IMMUNITY
An Inoculation
Eula Biss

A *New York Times* Best Seller and Finalist for the National Book Critics Circle Award

Named a Top Ten Book of the Year by the *Chicago Tribune*, *Entertainment Weekly*, *Los Angeles Times*, *Newsday*, *New York Magazine*, the *New York Times Book Review*, NPR's *Science Friday*, *Publishers Weekly*, and *Time Out New York*

In this bold, fascinating book, Eula Biss addresses our fear of the government, the medical establishment, and what may be in our children's air, food, mattresses, medicines, and vaccines. Reflecting on her own experience as a new mother, she suggests that we cannot immunize our children, or ourselves, against the world. As she explores the metaphors surrounding immunity, Biss extends her conversations with other mothers to meditations on the myth of Achilles, Voltaire's *Candide*, Bram Stoker's *Dracula*, Rachel Carson's *Silent Spring*, Susan Sontag's *AIDS and Its Metaphors*, and beyond. *On Immunity* is an inoculation against our fear and a moving account of how we are all interconnected—our bodies and our fates.

"*Subtle, spellbinding.... [Biss] advances from all sides, like a chess player, drawing on science, myth, literature to herd us to the only logical end, to vaccinate.*" —**The New York Times Book Review**

"*By exploring the anxieties about what's lurking inside our flu shots, the air, and ourselves, [Biss] drives home the message that we are all responsible for one another.* On Immunity *will make you consider that idea on a fairly profound level.*" —**Entertainment Weekly, Grade: A**

"*This elegant, intelligent and very beautiful book ... occupies a space between research and reflection, investigating our attitudes toward immunity and inoculation through a personal and cultural lens.*" —**Los Angeles Times**

ABOUT THE AUTHOR: **Eula Biss** is the author of *Notes from No Man's Land*, winner of the National Book Critics Circle Award in criticism, and *The Balloonists*. Her essays have appeared in the *Believer*, *Harper's Magazine*, and the *New York Times*.

September 2015 | Trade Paperback | Nonfiction | 224 pp | $16.00 | ISBN 9781555977207
Graywolf Press | graywolf.org | eulabiss.net

....

CONVERSATION STARTERS

1. *On Immunity* is dedicated to "other mothers," and Biss refers to her conversations with "other mothers" throughout the book. Is *On Immunity* a book specifically for mothers? For all parents? For everyone?

2. In the beginning of *On Immunity*, Eula Biss is uncertain about whether or not to fully vaccinate her child, and some of the other mothers she consults in the book choose not to vaccinate their children. By the book's end, Biss is decidedly pro-vaccination. How did she arrive at this position?

3. Why do you think Biss expresses empathy towards "anti-vaxxers"?

4. Biss states, "Those of us who draw on collective immunity owe our health to our neighbors" and "The health of our bodies always depends on choices other people are making." Beyond vaccination, what choices do other people make that your health depends on?

5. As Biss writes, the people who choose not to vaccinate their children are "more likely to be white, to have an older married mother with a college education, and to live in a household with an income of $75,000 or more." How is vaccination a class issue?

6. Have your opinions on vaccinations changed or shifted since reading the book? Why or why not?

7. How do the myths of Achilles and Narcissus help inform questions of individual responsibility vs. community responsibility?

8. Why do you think Biss chose to begin the book with the myth of Achilles and end it with the myth of Narcissus?

9. Biss examines ways in which language relieves or reinforces our medical anxieties. Are there certain words or metaphors that have influenced how you approach your health care decisions?

10. Biss notes a historic association between vampires and vaccinations. She quotes author Eric Nuzum, who says: "If you want to understand any moment in time, or any cultural moment, just look at their vampires." What do today's portrayals of vampires say about our moment in time?

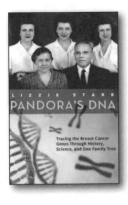

PANDORA'S DNA
Tracing the Breast Cancer Genes Through History, Science, and One Family Tree
Lizzie Stark

Would you cut out your healthy breasts and ovaries if you thought it might save your life? That's not a theoretical question for journalist Lizzie Stark's relatives, who grapple with the horrific legacy of cancer built into the family DNA. The BRCA mutation has robbed most of her female relatives of breasts, ovaries, peace of mind, or life itself. In *Pandora's DNA*, Stark uses her family's experience to frame a larger story about the so-called breast cancer genes, exploring the morass of legal quandaries, scientific developments, medical breakthroughs, and ethical concerns that surround the BRCA mutations. She explores topics from the troubling history of prophylactic surgery and the storied origins of the boob job to the landmark Supreme Court decision against Myriad Genetics. Although a genetic test for cancer risk may sound like the height of scientific development, the treatments remain crude and barbaric. Through her own experience, Stark shows what it's like to live in a brave new world where gazing into the crystal ball of genetics has many unintended consequences.

"Stark has both fully researched her subject and poured out her heart in this blend of history, science, and memoir . . . Most impressive, she tells her personal story with considerable frankness and flashes of humor." —**Kirkus Reviews**

"With her remarkable memoir, Stark gives us medical history and personal testament that intelligently balances hard-edged science with boundless hope." —**Publishers Weekly**

"An extraordinary book, written with passion and compassion, Pandora's DNA illuminates a new world of science and medicine." —**Siddhartha Mukherjee, author of *The Emperor of All Maladies: A Biography of Cancer***

ABOUT THE AUTHOR: **Lizzie Stark** is the author of *Leaving Mundania* and a freelance journalist who has written for io9.com, *The Today Show* website, *Psychology Today*, the *Daily Beast*, and the *Philadelphia Inquirer*.

October 2014 | Hardcover | Nonfiction | 336 pp | $26.95 | ISBN 9781613748602
Chicago Review Press | chicagoreviewpress.com | lizziestark.com/books/pandoras-dna/

CONVERSATION STARTERS

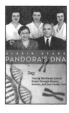

1. On page 6, Stark writes, "To me, my family's level of cancer feels biblical in scope, and this has mediated my personal experiences with the medical system." In what ways has Stark's family history affected her treatment?

2. On page 8, Stark quotes a study that showed that less than half of women with a BRCA diagnosis choose mastectomy. Why do you think this is?

3. The book's title draws a comparison between the BRCA genes and Pandora's box. One opened, Pandora's box let the plagues escape into the world; only hope was left in the bottom of the box. In what ways is this a metaphor for the BRCA genes?

4. The book explores the history of breast cancer, from women like the Persian queen Atossa up to the modern day. In what ways has the experience of breast cancer changed over time? In what ways has it stayed the same?

5. Do you think the Supreme Court made the right decision in overturning Myriad's patents on the BRCA genes, but upholding the possibility that cDNA is patentable? Why?

6. One aspect of the BRCA experience for both patients and physicians is the weight of uncertainty—uncertainty about a particular woman's risk levels and uncertainty due to the imperfect knowledge of medicine. How does this uncertainty impact Stark and her relatives throughout the book?

7. If Cheri had tested positive for a BRCA mutation, there is a good chance she would have had a preventive mastectomy. However, she was not offered testing because she did not have a first-degree relative with breast cancer. At the same time, genetic testing has very complicated emotional repercussions, even for those who, like Stark's cousin Lisa, test negative, and if it were more widely offered, this psychological stress would affect many more people, likely in unexpected ways. Do you think that genetic testing for BRCA mutations should be available on demand or only for selected populations? Why or why not?

8. People often say that "knowledge is power," but given the complex repercussions of understanding one has a BRCA mutation—a diagnosis for one person can mean stress for the entire rest of the family—is there also a right not to know?

PIGS CAN'T SWIM
A Memoir
Helen Peppe

A rollicking tale of survival as the youngest of nine children in hardscrabble backwoods Maine, as hilarious as it is heartbreaking

Everything on Helen Peppe's dirt-poor Maine farm was out of control: sibling rivalry, feral male chauvinism, sex in the hayloft, even the animals.

In telling her wild family story, Peppe shines, with deadpan humor, an unerring eye for the absurd, and poignant compassion for her utterly overwhelmed parents. While her resilience and candor will inevitably remind readers of Jeanette Wall or Mary Karr, Peppe's wry insight and moments of tenderness are entirely her own.

"*I love this book!*"—**Carolyn Chute, author of** *The Beans of Egypt Maine*

"*A writer and photographer's wry but poignant account of her hardscrabble childhood and adolescence in rural New England . . . Unsentimental in its character portrayals and forthright yet humorous in its depiction of devastated innocence and family dysfunction, Peppe's book is a celebration of difference, resilience and the healing power of love.*"—*Kirkus Review*

ABOUT THE AUTHOR: **Helen Peppe,** writer and photographer, lives near Portland Maine, with her two children, four dogs, eight rescued rabbits, four guinea pigs, and two destructive kittens.

February 2014 | Hardcover | Nonfiction | 272 pp | $22.99 | ISBN 9780306822728
February 2016 | Trade Paperback | Nonfiction | 288 pp | $14.99 | ISBN 9780306824234
Da Capo Press | dacapopress.com | helenpeppe.com

CONVERSATION STARTERS

1. Peppe identifies most locations by descriptions, and most people by characteristics (Blustery-and-favored Brother, Sister-who-holds-grudges-longer-than-God, Hair-twirling-pretty sister, tough-yet-admirable sister, Sad-tittering sister, and Sister of poor choices). Did this help you connect to the characters better?

2. Helen is an oddity in the family. She is the youngest, a vegetarian, an avid reader, and an animal lover. How do her siblings and parents treat her and communicate with her because of these differences?

3. We are shown a detailed view of rural Maine. The description comes from a child's perspective that is often light-hearted and humorous. Does the humor hide the depressing nature of how the family lives? Does the parents' love for their children outweigh the moments of neglect?

4. Helen is always immersed in a book and mentions that the fictional worlds of Stephen King always seemed so much safer than her own reality. What was it about her own reality that seemed so unsafe to her?

5. Peppe creates an insular world for her family, and only when the outside world intrudes do problems emerge. If this is the case, why are Helen and her siblings always trying to escape?

6. The title, Pigs Can't Swim, relates to Waterboro, the pig her brother picks up on their road trip. Even after the family sees Waterboro swimming, they still decide pigs can't swim. What does that show about the family?

7. Throughout the first half of the book, the tone is humorous and the child's perspective provides an innocent view of a life she has yet to question. As darker experiences are described—the hair-twirling-pretty sister's abusive relationship and Helen's molestation—the tone shifts. Did you notice this shift? How does the tone throughout relate to Helen's resilience?

8. Freedom is a main theme. The siblings are constantly trying to find ways to escape. Dakota provides Helen with physical freedom, books provide a mental escape, and Eric provides companionship and support. Where else does Helen search for freedom?

ROCK, MEET WINDOW
A Father-Son Story
Jason Good

A funny and poignant memoir that delves into the magic, fails, and meaning of fatherhood.

Humorist and family-man Jason Good is an only child with an atypical story to tell. His isn't the usual rant about how hard it is to be a modern father or a tale about a damaging relationship with his father. Jason grew up with a charismatic, communicative, affectionate, and frustrated political science professor for a father--a man who taught him most everything about how to be a dad, how to live. Jason was figuring out how to parent his own two young boys when his dad was diagnosed with cancer and told he had nine months to live. That moment, and the year that followed, inspired Jason to tell the story of something he had always taken for granted: how his father had earned his true friendship and admiration in adulthood by the way he had parented him to manhood.

Jason Good's book shows how an imperfect father can be perfection in all the ways that matter in the end, moving us to alternately hoot and become wet-eyed through his retelling of the friction points and lessons learned. Ultimately, this book inspires us to reconsider our own relationships and to appreciate the power of fatherhood.

Serious illness may have been the force to bring this father and son closer, but comedy ultimately infuses their shared sense of understanding, respect and camaraderie. **—Shelf Awareness for Readers**

ABOUT THE AUTHOR: **Jason Good** is a contributing writer to *The New York Times*, *Parents Magazine*, *GQ*, and *Psychology Today* and the blogger behind JasonGood.net. He is husband to a fantastic woman, and father to two sons. He works from home in a small, cold office with plenty of sunlight, and frequently wears noise canceling headphones. He lives in Minneapolis, Minnesota.

May 2015 | Hardcover | Nonfiction | 224 pp | $22.95 | ISBN 9781452129228
Chronicle Books | chroniclebooks.com | jasongood.net

CONVERSATION STARTERS

1. In which ways is Jason's relationship with his father similar or disimilar from your own relationship with your mother or father. Michael is a unique and interesting person, but is there anything unique about his relationship with Jason?

2. Was there a moment in your life when you suddenly saw your mother or father as a true adult – flaws and all?

3. If you have children, did becoming a parent help you understand your own parents more accurately, or provide you with a different perspective on them? What are they like as grandparents?

4. Does Jason idolize his father? Or does he have a healthy, reaslistic idea of who he is and his relationship to him.

5. What do you think of Jason's mother? Is she really as simple as he makes her out to be, or is there a depth to her that he perhaps left unexplored?

6. Michael experiences a difficult time with his brother Paul in relation to stem cell donation. Would you donate stem cells or bone marrow to a sibling? Is it OK for someone who doesn't trust traditional, western medicine to decline donating based on his or her own fears and suspicions?

7. Clement shared some personal emails with Michael in regards to this issue. Do you think it was right for him to do that? How do you imagine Gayle feels, knowing that her opinions were forwarded without her knowledge?

8. What do you think about the level of involvment Jason had with his father's illness?

9. Michael is very specfic that he doesn't care about a funeral. "What do I care? I'll be dead," he says. Do you believe him?

10. Have you cared for an ailing parent? How did it change your relationship with him or her?

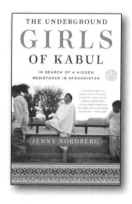

THE UNDERGROUND GIRLS OF KABUL

In Search of a Hidden Resistance in Afghanistan

Jenny Nordberg

Winner of the 2015 J. Anthony Lukas Book Prize

In The Underground Girls of Kabul, investigative journalist Jenny Nordberg uncovers a hidden custom that will transform your understanding of what it means to grow up as a girl in Afghanistan. In a culture ruled almost entirely by men, the birth of a son is cause for celebration, while the arrival of a daughter is often mourned as a misfortune. A *bacha posh* (literally translated from Dari as "dressed up like a boy") is a third kind of child – a girl temporarily raised as a boy and presented as such to the outside world. Nordberg, the reporter who broke the story of this phenomenon for the *New York Times*, constructs a powerful and moving account of those secretly living on the other side of a deeply segregated society where women have limited rights and freedom.

"Through extensive interviews with former bacha posh, observation of present ones and conversations with doctors and teachers, Nordberg unearths details of a dynamic that one suspects will be news to the armies of aid workers and gender experts in post-invasion Afghanistan." —**New York Times Book Review**

"Jenny Nordberg has produced a striking and nuanced work that explores the current status of Afghan women through one of their subcultures . . . [A] finely written book." —**Washington Post**

ABOUT THE AUTHOR: **Jenny Nordberg** is an award-winning journalist based in New York. A correspondent and columnist for Swedish national newspaper *Svenska Dagbladet*, she has a long record of investigative reports for, among others, the *New York Times*, where she also contributed to a series that won the 2005 Pulitzer Prize for National Reporting. In 2010, she was awarded the Robert F. Kennedy Award for Excellence in Journalism for a television documentary on Afghan women. She is a member of the International Consortium of Investigative Journalists (ICIJ).

July 2015 | Trade Paperback | Nonfiction | 384 pp | $15.00 | ISBN 9780307952509
Broadway Books | penguinrandomhouse.com | TheUndergroundGirlsOfKabul.com

....

CONVERSATION STARTERS

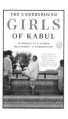

1. Before reading *Underground Girls of Kabul*, what (if anything) did you know about Afghanistan? Was there anything in the book you found surprising about the country and its history?

2. Do you think the practice of *bacha posh* is subversive, with the potential to change the strict gender culture of Afghanistan? Or do you see it as women capitulating to and reinforcing a system of segregation? Do people have the power to challenge Afghanistan's patriarchal society in other ways?

3. Does the practice of *bacha posh* make sense to you, or is it still entirely foreign? How would you explain why this happens?

4. Disguise is a common strategy for coping with subjugation. Can you think of any actual, real-life historical or present-day parallels to *bacha posh*? What examples are there of people of pretending to be someone or something else in response to segregation or oppression?

5. Many of the women in this book experience the limits of female freedom, even if they have had some success. Is there a limit to what most women can achieve, even in our own society today? Why is that?

6. Did you ever wonder how things would have been different had you been born a child of the other gender? Did you ever wish that you could be a different gender, even if only to deal with a particular circumstance?

7. In what way were you treated like a boy or a girl, respectively, when you were a child? Were you told that there were things you absolutely couldn't do because of your gender? Do you see a future where gender roles will be less strictly defined? What would that future offer us?

8. Do you agree with the author's conclusion that women's rights are essential to human rights and to building peaceful civilizations? Why or why not?

9. What would you tell the author or any of these women? They would love to hear from you. We invite you to continue the conversation on BachaPosh.com or to connect with Jenny Nordberg on Twitter: @nordbergj.

YOUNG ADULT

BEYOND MAGENTA
Transgender Teens Speak Out
Susan Kuklin

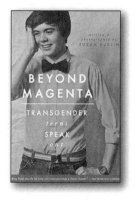

A groundbreaking and award-winning work of LGBT literature takes an honest look at the life, love, and struggles of transgender teens.

Author and photographer Susan Kuklin met and interviewed six transgender or gender-neutral young adults and used her considerable skills to represent them thoughtfully and respectfully before, during, and after their personal acknowledgment of gender preference. Portraits, family photographs, and candid images grace the pages, augmenting the emotional and physical journey each youth has taken. Each honest discussion and disclosure, whether joyful or heartbreaking, is completely different from the other because of family dynamics, living situations, gender, and the transition these teens make in recognition of their true selves.

"Downright revelatory. ... Kuklin captures these teenagers not as idealized exemplars of what it "means" to be transgender but as full, complex, and imperfect human beings." —Publishers Weekly (**starred review**)

"Informative, revealing, powerful and necessary." —Kirkus Reviews (**starred review**)

"Speaking with equal impact to both the reader's heart and mind, Beyond Magenta is highly recommended." —Booklist (**starred review**)

"An eye-opener" —The Huffington Post

"[A] candid, inspiring book." —The Chicago Tribune

ABOUT THE AUTHOR: **Susan Kuklin** is the award-winning author and photographer of more than thirty books for children and young adults that span social issues and culture. Her photographs have appeared in *Time*, *Newsweek*, and the *New York Times*. Susan Kuklin lives in New York City.

March 2015 | Trade Paperback | Young Adult | 192 pp | $12.99 | ISBN 9780763673680
Candlewick Press | candlewick.com | susankuklin.net

CONVERSATION STARTERS

1. What are some of the assumptions people make based on perceptions of gender? What pressures do family, friends, and society place on a person based on their perceived gender identity?

2. Jessy first came out as a lesbian, and later as trans. How did the two experiences differ? Was one more difficult than the other for Jessy? Why or why not?

3. During Jessy's early high-school years, he didn't know what the word transgender meant. "Hey, if you like women and you're a woman, then you're a lesbian" (7). How important is terminology in knowing one's self? Do you think kids today know more about gender diversity?

4. Christina was bullied in elementary and high school. Have you ever witnessed someone being bullied for being perceived as LGBTQ? What happened? What did you do?

5. Christina says, "I think the other students were freaked out because I looked like a girl and I was pressing against gender boundaries" (49). Why do you think some people get upset when someone challenges gender boundaries? Does it ever upset you?

6. Mariah says, "Everyone goes through one kind of transition or another. We go through transitions every day. Except mine is maybe a little extreme. I'm not at the end of my transition. I'm barely at the beginning" (91). What sorts of transitions has Mariah gone through in her life? What sorts of transitions have you gone through or think you will go through in the future?

7. Cameron says, "Being trans is not something that is accurately portrayed in the media" (112). What portrayals of transgender or gender-neutral people have you seen in the media? Are they accurate? Why or why not?

8. Why do you think Nat wanted to be photographed in black-and-white?

9. Photographs are a very important part of *Beyond Magenta*. What do you learn about each teen from looking at his, her, or their photographs?

10. Did reading this book change your understanding of gender identity? Why or why not?

THE CARNIVAL AT BRAY

Jessie Ann Foley

2015 Printz Honor Winner, ALA 2015 Top Ten BFYA, Morris Award Finalist, Kirkus Reviews' Best YA Book

The Carnival at Bray is an electrifying story of loss and triumph, family and adventure, and of the earth-shattering power of music and love from newcomer Jessie Ann Foley.

It's 1993, and Generation X pulses to the beat of Kurt Cobain and the grunge movement. Sixteen-year-old Maggie Lynch is uprooted from big-city Chicago to a windswept town on the Irish Sea. Surviving on care packages of Spin magazine and Twizzlers from her rocker uncle Kevin, she wonders if she'll ever find her place in this new world. When first love and sudden death simultaneously strike, a naive but determined Maggie embarks on a forbidden pilgrimage that will take her to a seedy part of Dublin and on to a life-altering night in Rome to fulfill a dying wish. Through it all, Maggie discovers an untapped inner strength to do the most difficult but rewarding thing of all—live.

"Carnival is earmarked to be a classic." **—San Diego Book Review**

"Every character, every place comes alive with crisp, precise detail. Powerfully evocative." **—Kirkus, Starred Review**

"This romantic and original book will be long remembered by its readers." **—VOYA**

"Foley sets the scene vividly, [and] the narrative voice is clear and compelling." **—School Library Journal**

"Beautifully-done coming of age story . . . as bittersweet as a first love and just as unforgettable." **—Jennie K., Forever Young Adult**

ABOUT THE AUTHOR: **Jessie Ann Foley** is a Chicago Public Schools English teacher. She holds an MFA in Fiction Writing from Columbia College Chicago. *The Carnival at Bray* is her first novel.

October 2014 | Trade Paperback | Young Adult | 240 pp | $12.95 | ISBN 9780989515597
Elephant Rock Books | elephantrockbooks.com | jessieannfoley.com

CONVERSATION STARTERS

1. *The Carnival at Bray* is written in third person. What access does the third-person point of view allow readers that they wouldn't have known in first person? Why do you think the author made this decision?

2. Ronnie asks Maggie a lot of age-inappropriate questions, to which Maggie responds, "I'll tell you when you're my age." How does Uncle Kevin's way of handling this compare to Maggie's? How does Maggie learn about what it means to be an adult?

3. Many of the characters in *The Carnival at Bray* are outsiders in some way. How does being an outsider in Ireland shape Maggie's identity? In what ways are the other characters in the novel outsiders?

4. How does Maggie's relationship with her mother, Laura, mature over the course of the book? What does Maggie understand about Laura at the end of the book that she didn't understand at the beginning?

5. How do the song lyrics and poems quoted throughout the novel shape your understanding of Maggie or the time in which she's living?

6. Mental illness is explored through Eoin's mother, Mary, Uncle Kevin, and Kurt Cobain. Discuss the way the author deals with mental illness in this novel.

7. How does Dan Sean mark the passage of time and the history of Bray in the novel?

8. When Maggie and Eoin run away to Rome, they essentially play house. Laura is often described as doing much of the same with Colm. What do you think Maggie learns about love and relationships from her mother, and where do you think she makes an effort to do something different?

9. How are images of the natural world (e.g., the water surrounding Bray or the Italian countryside) used to set the tone of certain scenes?

10. When Maggie decides to travel to Rome to see Nirvana as per Uncle Kevin's instructions, Dan Sean dubs it a pilgrimage. Throughout the novel, she prays to Uncle Kevin for guidance. Discuss Maggie's faith, whether it be in religion, Cobain, love, or Kevin.

CRENSHAW
Katherine Applegate

In her first novel since winning the Newbery Medal, Katherine Applegate delivers an unforgettable and magical story about family, friendship, and resilience.

Jackson and his family have fallen on hard times. There's no more money for rent. And not much for food, either. His parents, his little sister, and their dog may have to live in their minivan. Again.

Crenshaw is a cat. He's large, he's outspoken, and he's imaginary. He has come back into Jackson's life to help him. But is an imaginary friend enough to save this family from losing everything?

Crenshaw proves in unexpected ways that friends matter, whether real or imaginary.

*"This accessible and moving novel demonstrates how the creative resilience of a child's mind can soften difficult situations, while exploring the intersection of imagination and truth." —****Publishers Weekly,*** **starred review**

ABOUT THE AUTHOR: **Katherine Applegate** is the author of the bestselling Animorphs series, and the novels *Home of the Brave* and *The One and Only Ivan*, winner of the 2013 Newbery Medal. She lives with her husband, author Michael Grant, and their two children in Northern California.

September 2015 | Hardcover | Middle Grade | 256 pp | $16.99 | ISBN 9781250043238
Macmillan Children's Publishing Group | crenshawthebook.com

CONVERSATION STARTERS

1. Discuss Jackson's statement: "Stories are lies, when you get right down to it. And I don't like being lied to." Why doesn't Jackson like made-up stories? Why is it so important for him to have a logical explanation for everything that happens?

2. When are the times in Jackson's life that Crenshaw appears? Which events occur that create a need for Jackson to have Crenshaw in his life? Discuss Jackson's comment about the name Crenshaw: "It felt like a blank piece of paper before you draw on it."

3. Why does Jackson feel different from the other members of his family? Describe scenes in the story where Jackson feels separate from them. Identify times in the story when Jackson realizes how important his family is to him.

4. When did Crenshaw go away in Jackson's life earlier? Why has he never told Marisol about Crenshaw and about his family's problems? Why does he tell her now?

5. Discuss the theme of friendship in this book. How did Jackson and Marisol become friends? What are the experiences and beliefs that they have in common? What are their differences? How does their friendship help each of them?

6. Why does Jackson steal the dog cookie? How does he feel about the few times that he has stolen from a store? Why does he feel worse about lying than stealing? What makes him ask Crenshaw: "Are you my conscience?"

7. Discuss the theme of magic in this story. What is the meaning of "magic" in the context of Jackson's life? Why did he want to reveal how the magician's tricks worked at school? Discuss Marisol's comment: "Just enjoy the magic while you can, okay?"

8. Jackson sometimes feels as if he is the most grownup member of his family. Identify times in the story when he does appear to act more grown-up than his parents. Identify places in the story when his parents are in charge of the situation.

EGG AND SPOON
Gregory Maguire

In this tour de force, master storyteller Gregory Maguire offers a dazzling novel for fantasy lovers of all ages.

Elena Rudina lives in the impoverished Russian countryside. Her father has been dead for years. One of her brothers has been conscripted into the Tsar's army, the other taken as a servant in the house of the local landowner. Her mother is dying. And there is no food. But then a train arrives in the village, a train carrying untold wealth, a cornucopia of food, and a noble family destined to visit the Tsar in Saint Petersburg — a family that includes Ekaterina, a girl of Elena's age. When the two girls' lives collide, an adventure is set in motion, an escapade that includes mistaken identity, a monk locked in a tower, a prince traveling incognito, and — in a starring role only Gregory Maguire could have conjured — Baba Yaga, witch of Russian folklore, in her ambulatory house perched on chicken legs.

"Egg and Spoon is a beautiful reminder that fairy tales are at their best when they illuminate the precarious balance between lighthearted childhood and the darkness and danger of adulthood." —School Library Journal (starred review)

"An epic"—**Kirkus Reviews (starred review)**

"Rich story." —**Publishers Weekly (starred review)**

"[T]here is so much in his rich and consistently surprising prose" —**The Horn Book (starred review)**

"An enticing mix of mystery, danger and magic." —**Shelf Awareness (starred review)**

ABOUT THE AUTHOR: **Gregory Maguire** is the author of the incredibly popular books including *Wicked: The Life and Times of the Wicked Witch of the West*, which inspired the musical. He is also the author of several books for children, including *What-the-Dickens*, a *New York Times* bestseller. Gregory Maguire lives outside Boston.

August 2015 | Trade Paperback | Young Adult | 496 pp | $11.99 | ISBN 9780763680169
Candlewick Press | candlewick.com | gregorymaguire.com

CONVERSATION STARTERS

1. As the story unfolds, the narrator reveals more and more about himself. Does your opinion of him change along the way? How trustworthy is he? How likable? Why does he risk so much for Elena?

2. What are the major differences that divide Elena and Cat at the beginning of *Egg & Spoon*? By the end, what are their common bonds?

3. The Firebird is described as the "bright soul of all the Russias" (4). What does that mean? How can a country have a soul? Does America have one?

4. Great-Aunt Sophia has gone to enormous trouble and expense so that Cat can be introduced to the Tsar's godson. Why? What does the older woman want for her niece? What does Cat want for herself?

5. "Ambition without direction," Peter Petrovich tells Elena (28), "is like milk without a cup." What does he mean by this? Which characters in the novel prove his point? How?

6. Russian aristocrats in this novel seem more likely to speak French than Russian. What does this suggest about their attachment to their homeland? They also tend to doubt the existence of Baba Yaga and the Firebird. Why?

7. "I *am* life," says Baba Yaga (144) soon after she meets Cat. What do you think she means by that? Do you agree with her? Why or why not?

8. Baba Yaga's wicked wit sometimes flies right over the heads of her listeners. What are some of her jokes that you caught? What are some of her zany, comic anachronisms (puns, references, or quotes from our time, not Tsarist Russia's)? Which are your favorites? Why?

9. "There is enough world for everyone," says the dragon (386). "But everyone cries in want of more." Do you agree? Why is it so difficult to know the difference between enough and *more* than enough?

10. What is the significance of the title? Does it refer to one particular egg in this novel full of remarkable eggs? What connection does an egg have with a spoon? "Does being in possession of a spoon give you more right to the egg?" the narrator asks (188). What do you think?

THE EVOLUTION OF CALPURNIA TATE

Jacqueline Kelly

Calpurnia Virginia Tate is eleven years old in 1899 when she wonders why the yellow grasshoppers in her Texas backyard are so much bigger than the green ones. With a little help from her notoriously cantankerous grandfather, Callie explores the natural world around her and comes up against just what it means to be a girl at the turn of the century.

"The most delightful historical novel . . . Fresh, funny, and poignant."
—The New Yorker

THE CURIOUS WORLD OF CALPURNIA TATE

Whether wrangling a rogue armadillo or stray dog, a guileless younger brother or standoffish cousin, Callie Vee and her escapades will have readers laughing and crying in this return to Fentress, Texas. Travis keeps bringing home strays. And Callie has her hands full keeping the animals—her brother included—away from her mother's critical eye. Will she succeed?

"A warm, welcome stand-alone companion." —**Kirkus Reviews**, starred review

About the Author: **Jacqueline Kelly** won the Newbery Honor for her first book, *The Evolution of Calpurnia Tate*. She was born in New Zealand, raised in Canada, attended college in El Paso and medical school in Galveston. After practicing medicine for many years, she went to law school at the University of Texas and practiced law before realizing she wanted to write fiction. She now makes her home with her husband and various cats and dogs in Austin and Fentress, Texas.

The Evolution of Calpurnia Tate
January 2011 | Trade Paperback | Middle Grade | 352 pp | $7.99 | ISBN 9780312659301
The Curious World of Calpurnia Tate
July 2015 | Hardcover | Middle Grade | 320 pp | $16.99 | ISBN 9780805097443
Macmillan Children's Publishing Group | calpurniatatebooks.com

THE EVOLUTION OF CALPURNIA TATE

1. What are some of the advantages Calpurnia enjoys as the only girl in her family of seven children?

2. Why is Calpurnia so annoyed by her brothers' interest in Lula? How does Calpurnia decide to handle the situation?

3. How do Calpurnia and her grandfather make their initial connection? What is Grandfather's reaction to Calpurnia's interest in the natural world?

4. Why don't Calpurnia and Lula ever have to perform in another recital after their first one? What is their reaction to the news?

5. Why is Calpurnia upset with Harry when she discovers he is courting Miss Minerva Goodacre? What does Calpurnia do about it that causes Harry to be angry with her?

THE CURIOUS WORLD OF CALPURNIA TATE

1. Why do the people in Fentress and the mayor of Galveston refuse to listen to Captain Tate's prediction about the storm? Why is he so sure the storm is going to occur? What other options does Captain Tate have to warn the people?

2. When Calpurnia's grandfather begins to teach Calpurnia about air pressure, he has Calpurnia make a barometer even though he already has one. Calpurnia says, "This is going to be one of those lessons about learning something from the ground up" (30). What does she mean by that statement? What other lessons does she learn from the ground up?

3. Why is Aggie so unfriendly toward Calpurnia? How does Calpurnia negotiate with Aggie to get what she wants from Aggie?

4. How do Calpurnia and her grandfather try to help Travis overcome his repulsion of blood and guts? Why is it important for him to be able to look at blood without getting sick?

5. How does Calpurnia prove to Dr. Pritzker that she can handle the job of his assistant? Why is Dr. Pritzker so surprised by Calpurnia's actions and knowledge?

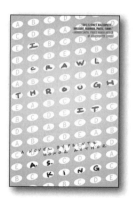

I CRAWL THROUGH IT

A. S. King

Four teenagers are on the verge of exploding. The anxieties they face at every turn have nearly pushed them to the point of surrender: senseless high-stakes testing, the lingering damage of past trauma, the buried grief and guilt of tragic loss. They are desperate to cope, but no one is listening.

So they will lie. They will split in two. They will turn inside out. They will even build an invisible helicopter to fly themselves far away...but nothing releases the pressure. Because, as they discover, the only way to truly escape their world is to fly right into it.

The genius of acclaimed author A.S. King reaches new heights in this groundbreaking work of surrealist fiction; it will mesmerize readers with its deeply affecting exploration of how we crawl through traumatic experience-and find the way out.

"I Crawl Through It *proves that A.S. King is one of the most innovative and talented novelists of our time. This is King's masterpiece—a brilliant, paranoid, poetic, funny, and at times overwhelmingly sad literary cocktail of absinthe and Adderall. What a trip!"* —**Andrew Smith, acclaimed author of** *Winger* **and** *Grasshopper Jungle*

"*At once a statement on the culture of modern schools as well as mental health issues, this novel is an ambitious, haunting work of art.*" —*School Library Journal*, **starred review**

"*A novel full of provocative ideas and sharply observed thoughts about the pressures society places on teenagers, especially girls.*" —*Publishers Weekly*, **starred review**

About the Author: **A.S. King** is the author of the highly acclaimed books *Glory O'Brien's History of the Future*; *Reality Boy*; *Ask the Passengers*, a Los Angeles Times Book Prize winner; *Everybody Sees the Ants*; and the Edgar Award nominated, Michael L. Printz Honor book *Please Ignore Vera Dietz*. She lives in Pennsylvania.

September 2015 | Hardcover | Young Adult | 336 pp | $18.00 | ISBN 9780316334099
Little, Brown Books for Young Readers | theNOVL.com | as-king.com

CONVERSATION STARTERS

1. The novel's narrators are all burdened by unacknowledged trauma. How do they each attempt to cope with it? Why are their initial methods unsuccessful?

2. How do the characters' surreal descriptions of dealing with pain—for example, Stanzi "splitting" herself and China turning herself "inside-out"—hint at the root of their trauma?

3. Kenneth, the bush man, appears throughout the novel as an alternately menacing and understanding character. He sells letters for kisses but also offers cryptic advice. What do you think his character represents? Is he ultimately a helpful figure or does he signify a false solution to life's problems?

4. When describing themselves, the protagonists speak only of their inadequacies and low self-esteem. Yet they eventually reveal a deep love for one another. What do the outside perspectives on Stanzi, China, and Lansdale reveal about their true abilities?

5. Why do the characters send bomb threats to the school?

6. When Stanzi and Gustav travel to "The Place of Arrivals," they expect to find a land of geniuses—a paradise free of tests and absentee parents. Instead, they come to realize that the community is equally oppressive, and its inhabitants look down on the outside world. What do you think this land represents?

7. Patricia is the only adult narrator, and she appears later than the other main characters. The reader never learns her full backstory, but she is instrumental in helping Stanzi and Gustav realize the dangers of The Place of Arrivals. Why do you think A.S. King includes her perspective?

8. Near the end of the novel, China states in upside down text, "The world will be upside down forever. We have to come to terms with this." What does this statement suggest about her path towards healing?

9. How do you interpret the novel's title?

10. Rather than telling the story in a straightforward manner, King creates an incredibly surreal and dreamlike universe. Why might she have decided to frame the novel this way? What are the benefits of this writing style?

INK AND ASHES
Valynne E. Maetani

Claire Takata has never known much about her father, who passed away ten years ago. But on the anniversary of his death, she finds a letter from her deceased father to her stepfather. Before now, Claire never had a reason to believe they even knew each other.

Struggling to understand why her parents kept this surprising history hidden, Claire combs through anything that might give her information about her father . . . until she discovers that he was a member of the yakuza, a Japanese organized crime syndicate. The discovery opens a door that should have been left closed.

The race to outrun her father's legacy reveals secrets of his past that cast ominous shadows, threatening Claire, her friends and family, her newfound love, and ultimately her life. Winner of Tu Books' New Visions Award, *Ink and Ashes* is a fascinating debut novel packed with romance, intrigue, and heart-stopping action.

"The novel's twists and turns will keep readers riveted and guessing even after they finish the book. This fantastic debut packs a highly suspenseful blend of action, intrigue, and teen romance." —**Kirkus Reviews** (**starred review**)

"Mystery lovers won't be able to put down Maetani's smartly written debut . . . This thoroughly engaging tale in the tradition of Nancy Drew or Veronica Mars ends on a satisfying note, but readers will hope for a sequel because it's just that good." —**School Library Journal**

"Full of character, culture, and suspense, Ink and Ashes is a fascinating read with surprising new elements and a true heroine in Claire Takata." —**Ally Condie, New York Times bestselling author of the MATCHED trilogy**

ABOUT THE AUTHOR: **Valynne Maetani** is a debut novelist from Utah. In a former life, she was a project manager and developed educational software for children with learning disabilities. Maetani is a member of the We Need Diverse Books team and is dedicated to promoting diversity in children's literature.

June 2015 | Hardcover | Young Adult | 368 pp | $19.95 | ISBN 9781620142110
Tu Books/Lee & Low Books | leeandlow.com | valynne.com

CONVERSATION STARTERS

1. How does Maetani use Claire's letters to her father throughout the book to demonstrate how Claire has changed? How is Claire the narrator different from Claire the letter writer? What do you think accounts for this difference?

2. What reasons motivate Claire's mother to keep the information about her husband from her children? Is she selfish or selfless in keeping this information? What would you do if you were in her position?

3. What are some signs that Claire's father was a part of the yakuza? What made the yakuza life attractive to Claire's father? Do you think his family and economic circumstances excuse or justify his decision to join the yakuza?

4. Why might Claire's father, Henry Sato, decide to become a judge after leaving the yakuza? How might his experiences in the yakuza help him in his new career as a judge? Is it appropriate for him to be a judge? Do a judge and a member of the yakuza have similar visions or interpretations of justice?

5. How does shame influence both Chase and Arakaki to hurt Claire? What are the roots of their perceived dishonor, respectively? Why do they think hurting Claire will help them find closure? Do you think revenge can bring closure?

6. At several points throughout the novel, Claire struggles with whom to trust. When her stepfather asks if she trusts him, she wonders, "If I felt his love, did that also mean I trusted him?" Do you think that love and trust are always the same? Is it possible to love someone without trusting them, or without knowing the whole truth about them?

7. If Claire were to write one more letter to her father at the end of the book, what do you think she would say or ask him? Do you think she would forgive and accept him or has too much changed?

8. Maetani has said she wanted to create a book she never got to read: a contemporary title with a Japanese protagonist. In your opinion, does the book reinforce or shatter stereotypes of Japanese culture?

9. The book ends with most questions answered, but Maetani leaves the door open for a sequel. Would you want to read a sequel to *Ink and Ashes*? If so, what do you hope would happen in it?

NINE OPEN ARMS
Benny Lindelauf

Nine Open Arms, a vivid historical novel, is compellingly mysterious as well as dramatic, humorous, and entertaining. A ghost story, a fantasy, and a family saga all wrapped into one, the novel begins with the Boon family's move to an isolated, dilapidated house that seems to have turned its back on the world.

It is 1937, and nine people set out for the middle of nowhere: a house at the end of a long, dusty road. Is it the site of a haunting tragedy, as one daughter believes, or an end to all their worries, as their father hopes?

The novel's gripping language plunges the reader into the world of a large, colorful, motherless family that finds itself teetering between different times and places.

"Every element of the tale has a purpose, and in the end, the multiple layers of past and present separate and come together in surprising, often discomfiting twists and turns. . . A challenging and entirely unique Dutch import."
—*Kirkus Reviews*, STARRED REVIEW

"Lindelauf's masterful rendering of fraught yet loving sisterly ties, snappy dialogue, graveyard mysteries, and "traces of a tragical tragedy" from generations past combine to humorous and poignant effect in this gripping tale of eclectic families and inveterate wanderers in search of a welcoming home."
—*Publishers Weekly*, STARRED REVIEW

ABOUT THE AUTHOR: **Benny Lindelauf** was born 15th December 1964 and grew up caught between two siblings. Inspired by his grandmother's storytelling, he wrote all his life, but didn't publish his first book until he'd tried many other things first: social work, theater school, creative dance, youth productions. But writing seems to be what he's best at.

Imagination, wit and drama are crucial ingredients in Benny's stories. Lindelauf said: "Writing is like moving from one house to the next over and over again." In *Nine Open Arms*, the writing moves through many rooms and houses, even worlds.

June 2014 | Hardcover | Young Adult | 264 pp | $16.95 | ISBN 9781592701469
Enchanted Lion Books | enchantedlion.com | bennylindelauf.com/en

CONVERSATION STARTERS

1. The three parts of the book have distinct tones and purpose, but the multiple layers and time periods eventually connect. Why do you think the author chose to structure the book this way? How did it affect how you read the book? One of the father's mottos is "First believe, then see." How do you see that applying to the overall story, and your own reading experience?

2. Fing is not an omniscient narrator since she learns the stories one by one from Oma Mei. Did you feel more connected to Fing because you were figuring out the story at the same time?

3. Who, or what, do you consider the main character? Why?

4. Nine Open Arms becomes a symbol for the many themes running throughout the book: displacement, determination, loss, love, and hope. Which characters in the book experience these emotions most strongly?

5. This book includes a "tragical tragedy," historical fiction, mystery, magical realism, humor, intricate plots, and a love story. If you were to describe the type of book it is to a friend, what would you call it? Where should it be located in a bookstore?

6. The author and translator provide a translator's note, a character list, a slang word list, a map, and a contents page. Did these additional pieces inform how you read the book? Did you find yourself referencing them often? Do they relate thematically to the interwoven narrative?

7. At the end of the book, what are the strongest characteristics of the family members? What does Fing come to understand about her family?

8. What do you think will come next for these characters? Consider the time period. Could WWII affect this somewhat magical folkloric world? What has the narrative thread about the travelers already taught us about "otherness" in Europe at this time?

9. Did knowing the book was a translation effect how you read the book? Or, if you did not realize it was a translation, does it change how you think back to it now?

NOT IF I SEE YOU FIRST
Eric Lindstrom

Parker Grant doesn't need 20/20 vision to see right through you. That's why she created the Rules: Don't treat her any differently just because she's blind, and *never* take advantage. There will be no second chances. Just ask Scott Kilpatrick, the boy who broke her heart.

When Scott suddenly reappears in her life after being gone for years, Parker knows there's only one way to react—shun him so hard it hurts. She has enough on her mind already, like trying out for the track team (that's right, her eyes don't work but her legs still do), doling out tough-love advice to her painfully naive classmates, and giving herself gold stars for every day she hasn't cried since her dad's death three months ago. But avoiding her past quickly proves impossible, and the more Parker learns about what really happened—both with Scott, and her dad—the more she starts to question if things are always as they seem. Maybe, just maybe, some Rules are meant to be broken.

"Thoughtful and honest, with characters that made me laugh, cry, and surprised me at every turn. It's a book I'll recommend for years to come."
—**Kody Keplinger, bestselling author of *The DUFF***

"A beautiful story about love, loss, friendship, and the difference between looking and truly seeing." —**Jennifer Brown, author of *Hate List***

"This book is fierce, funny, and honest. And get ready for some of the most likable characters you've read in years." —**Deb Caletti, National Book Award finalist**

"Parker Grant is unforgettable: vivid, feisty, and absolutely loveable. This book broke my heart, but left me smiling." —**Fiona Wood, author of *Wildlife* and *Six Impossible Things***

ABOUT THE AUTHOR: **Eric Lindstrom** is a BAFTA and WGA-nominated veteran of the interactive entertainment industry. *Not if I See You First* is his debut novel.

December 2015 | Hardcover | Young Adult | 320 pp | $18.00 | ISBN 9780316259859
Poppy | Little, Brown and Company | theNOVL.com | ericlindstrombooks.com

CONVERSATION STARTERS

1. As the novel is told from the perspective of a blind narrator, the characters are not introduced with the usual physical descriptions that authors often rely upon. What are some unconventional descriptors that Eric Lindstrom uses?

2. How do people intentionally and unintentionally break Parker's Rules? How does Parker's reliance on her rules change over the course of the novel?

3. Rule #11 is: "Don't be weird." Why is this rule important to Parker, and why might it be a challenging one for the people in Parker's life?

4. Parker claims that she "tells it like it is" and practices tough love, but sometimes her opinions come across as abrasive or mean. How do you differentiate between being honest and being kind?

5. What factors contribute to the tension in Parker's relationship with Aunt Celia? What might Celia's perspective be on their situation?

6. Why does Parker wear blindfolds? What do you think the blindfolds symbolize?

7. Once Parker learns the truth about Scott's middle school "prank," she second-guesses her initial reaction to the incident. Do you believe the depth of Parker's anger was justified at the time? Should she have forgiven Scott sooner, or did she make the right decision?

8. Even after Parker has forgiven Scott, he doesn't want to be friends with her. Do you believe his reasoning is justified?

9. What insights did you get from the novel about the life of someone navigating the world as a blind person? What insights did you get about navigating the world as a typical teenager?

10. The title on the book jacket is *Not if I See You First*, but the Braille says something different. Decipher the Braille. Now that you've read Parker Grant's story, what does this second message mean to you?

OFF THE PAGE
Jodi Picoult and Samantha Van Leer

New from the #1 *New York Times* bestselling authors, Jodi Picoult and her daughter and co-author, Samantha Van Leer! Meet Oliver, a prince literally taken from the pages of a fairy tale and transported into the real world. Meet Delilah, the girl who wished Oliver into being. It's a miracle that seems perfect at first—but then everything gets turned upside down.

Full of humor and witty commentary about life, *Off the Page* is a standalone novel as well as the companion to the authors' bestseller, *Between the Lines*, and is perfect for readers looking for a fairy-tale ending. Fans of Sarah Dessen and Meg Cabot are sure to appreciate this novel about love, romance, and relationships.

"A fun, fairy-tale romance for teens who believe in happily ever after."
—**School Library Journal**

"A quiet, lovely fairy-tale emphasizing the importance of family and creativity."
—**Booklist**

"Fairy-tale sweet." —**Kirkus Reviews**

ABOUT THE AUTHOR: **Jodi Picoult** is the author of 23 novels, including the #1 *New York Times* bestsellers *Leaving Time*, *The Storyteller*, *Lone Wolf*, *Sing You Home*, *House Rules*, *Handle with Care*, *Change of Heart*, *Nineteen Minutes*, and *My Sister's Keeper*. She also cowrote the #1 *New York Times* bestseller *Between the Lines*, the companion to *Off the Page*, with her daughter, Samantha van Leer. Jodi lives in New Hampshire with her husband and three children.

Samantha van Lee is a sophomore at Vassar College majoring in psychology with a minor in human development. She cowrote the #1 *New York Times* bestseller *Between the Lines*, the companion novel to *Off the Page*, with her mother, Jodi Picoult.

Jodi and Samantha have four dogs: Alvin, Harvey, Dudley, and Oliver, for whom the prince in this story is named.

May 2015 | Hardcover | Young Adult | 384 pp | $19.99 | ISBN 9780553535563
Delacorte Press | penguinrandomhouse.com | jodipicoult.com

CONVERSATION STARTERS

Cliques
1. Why do you think that people tend to be friends with others who are like them?

2. How are you and your friends similar to or different from each other?

Appearance
3. What is the significance of physical appearance in Delilah's world versus the world of Oliver's fairy tale?

4. How does the author use changes in each character's physical appearance to illustrate his or her development?

Fate
5. What role does Fate play in the novel, for the characters in Oliver's fairy tale and the characters in Delilah's world?

6. What role do you believe Fate plays in your own life, and in the lives of those around you?

Love
7. What are some times when Delilah, Oliver, and Edgar question the true nature of love?

8. How do you think each character would define love by the end of the novel? Do you agree with one of their definitions?

Family
9. Based on his interactions with other characters, who would Oliver consider to be his family?

10. Who are the people you consider to be your family, and why?

Freedom
11. Does the fairy tale represent freedom and escape, or does it trap the characters inside it?

12. Do you think Oliver, Edgar, and Delilah find the freedom they are searching for?

Reader
13. What is the relationship between an author, the characters, and the reader?

14. What is the role of imagination in storytelling?

THE SCORPION RULES
Erin Bow

Greta is a Duchess and Crown Princess—and a hostage to peace. This is how the game is played: if you want to rule, you must give one of your children as a hostage. And you must keep the peace; start a war and your hostage dies.

Greta will be free if she can survive until her eighteenth birthday. Until then she is prepared to die with dignity, if she must. But everything changes when a new hostage arrives, a boy who refuses to play by the rules, a boy who defies everything Greta has ever been taught. A boy who opens Greta's eyes to the brutality of the system they live under—and to her own power.

With her nation on the verge of war, Greta becomes a target in a new kind of game. A game that will end up killing her—unless she can find a way to break all the rules.

"This is fearfully superlative storytelling—electrical tension crackles in every elegant word. The finest fiction I've read this year." —**Elizabeth Wein, author of Code Name Verity**

"Bow's amoral artificial intelligence overlord is one of my favorite characters in a while." —**Maggie Stiefvater, author of The Raven Boys**

"One of the most inventive, devious, exciting, and thoroughly enjoyable books I've read in years. Very highly recommended!" —**Jonathan Maberry, New York Times bestselling author of Rot & Ruin**

ABOUT THE AUTHOR: **Erin Bow** is a physicist turned poet turned children's novelist—and she's won major awards in all three roles. She's the author of the acclaimed Russian-flavored fantasy *Plain Kate*, which received two starred reviews and was a YALSA Best Book of the Year, and the terrifying YA ghost story *Sorrow's Knot*, which received five starred reviews and was a *Kirkus Reviews* Best Book of the Year.

September 2015 | Hardcover | Young Adult | 384 pp | $17.99 | ISBN 9781481442718
Margaret K. McElderry Books | SimonandSchuster.com | ErinBow.com

CONVERSATION STARTERS

1. What genre would you consider *The Scorpion Rules* to be?

2. The Children of Peace have been trained to behave in a dignified manner, even when they are facing death. Do you think this training is cruel?

3. The political conflict in *The Scorpion Rules* is about access to fresh water. Discuss whether this seems plausible.

4. Is Talis a multidimensional character? How does the author present him as male even though he inhabits a female body?

5. Greta finds herself falling in love with Xie while she is also drawn to Elián. Do you think it's natural that she could care for both of them? Does it seem to matter in their society?

6. Discuss the following quote from Chapter 11: "You cannot control a man if you take everything from him. You must leave him something to lose." Is there a certain freedom that comes from being unencumbered?

7. The Abbot is a Class Two Artificial Intelligence with full rights of personhood. How does the Abbot demonstrate human qualities?

8. In Chapter 8, shortly after Elián's arrival, Greta says, "I had changed." How has her relationship with the Abbot and her mother shaped her character? How has knowing Elián helped cause these changes?

9. Xie and Elián tell Greta that they think about escaping all the time, but Greta has never thought about it. Is it because she thinks being a Child of Peace is her destiny, or is she just resigned to her fate?

10. As the story progresses, Greta begins to discover and claim her power. Are you worried that once she has joined Talis she will misuse her authority?

11. Almost as soon as Cumberlanders invade the Precepture, Tolliver Burr begins planning Greta's torture with the apple press. Why is torture one of the rituals of war? Do you think torture always gets "results"?

12. Do you agree with Greta that Elián is being stupid for challenging the status quo, or is he being heroic, like Spartacus?

13. In Chapter 20, after the Abbot tells Greta there might be an alternative to dying, she thinks: "Stirring inside me was the kind of fear that comes with hope." What does Greta mean? Do you think that hope can inspire fear?

THE SILENCED
James DeVita

Wisconsin Library Association 2008 Outstanding Book

2008-2009 Bookpage Notable Title

Marena struggles to remember what life was like before the Zero Tolerance Party installed listening devices in every home. Before they murdered her mother and put her father under house arrest. A time when difference was celebrated.

When the new Minister of Education cracks down in her school, Marena decides she has to fight back. Fueled by her memories and animated by her mother's spirit, Marena forms a resistance group—the White Rose. With little more than words, Marena defies the state officers lurking around every corner and embarks on a campaign of life-affirming civil disobedience.

The Silenced draws on the true story of Sophie Scholl and the White Rose, a movement that courageously resisted the Nazis. In an era when new technologies are accompanied by increasing surveillance, this is a powerfully relevant story of the enormous change that is possible when one person is courageous enough to speak the truth to power.

"This is far and away the best young adult novel I have read for years . . . It has a marvelously vibrant and courageous young heroine, and friends who may betray or help—hard to predict. Best of all it is based on one of the most ultimately tough young women to grace this earth." —**Louise Erdrich**

"Tautly plotted novel ... ripe for discussion." —***Kirkus Reviews***

"Gripping suspense combined with satisfyingly capable teen characters make this a good YA read ... a convincing dystopia." —***Booklist***

ABOUT THE AUTHOR: **James DeVita**, an author and actor, has published two award-winning novels for young readers as well as numerous plays. He is the recipient of the National Endowment for the Arts Literature Fellowship and lives in Wisconsin with his wife and two children.

August 2015 | Trade Paperback | Young Adult | 448 pp | $12.00 | ISBN 9781571319371
Milkweed Editions | milkweed.org | jamesdevita.com

CONVERSATION STARTERS

1. Marena's mother told her, "Every thing of beauty… is a form of resistance." Later in the novel, these words catch the attention of Mr. Greengritch. How does beauty counter the aims of the Zero Tolerance Party (ZT)?

2. Marena claims that she would rather die than betray her loved ones. Is there any space in the resistance for a lesser level of commitment?

3. Three families are presented in the novel: Marena's, Dex's, and Mr. Greengritch's. How do their families influence these characters? What is the ZT's interest in family ties?

4. Marena struggles to remember her life before the ZT took over. What is the importance of memory for Marena? For Mr. Greengritch?

5. While the novel is largely about Marena, Mr. Greengritch also narrates several sections. Why is his perspective important? In what ways is his character both juxtaposed with and parallel to Marena?

6. When Mr. Greengritch takes over Marena's class, he gives them a writing assignment: to describe what they think is "absolutely true" about themselves (69). What is the purpose of this assignment? What does he expect to learn about the students?

7. The Zero Tolerance Party revoked labor visas and created a "racial purity index." What threat does the ZT imagine is posed by the people they classify as "deficient"? Although the novel is overtly focused on free speech, how does the underlying narrative about race and citizenship status complicate this theme?

8. While *The Silenced* was inspired by the real White Rose resistance movement in Nazi Germany, the novel is set in a recognizable near future. What methods of state control and surveillance are present in the world of the novel, and how do they compare to those used in our world today?

THE STRANGE AND BEAUTIFUL SORROWS OF AVA LAVENDER
Leslye Walton

Magical realism, lyrical prose, and the pain and passion of human love haunt this hypnotic generational saga.

Foolish love appears to be the Roux family birthright, an ominous forecast for its most recent progeny, Ava Lavender. Ava — in all other ways a normal girl — is born with the wings of a bird. In a quest to understand her peculiar disposition and a growing desire to fit in with her peers, sixteen-year old Ava ventures into the wider world, ill-prepared for what she might discover and naive to the twisted motives of others. Others like the pious Nathaniel Sorrows, who mistakes Ava for an angel and whose obsession with her grows until the night of the summer solstice celebration. That night, the skies open up, rain and feathers fill the air, and Ava's quest and her family's saga build to a devastating crescendo. First-time author Leslye Walton has constructed a layered and unforgettable mythology of what it means to be born with hearts that are tragically, exquisitely human.

"[A]n entrancing and sumptuously written multigenerational novel."
—Publishers Weekly (starred review)

"A unique book, highly recommended for readers looking for something a step away from ordinary."—**School Library Journal (starred review)**

"Walton presents challenges that most teens will hopefully never face. She writes of love, betrayal, birth, murder, affection and rape—and wraps them in prose so radiant that readers feel carried by Ava's narrative."
—Shelf Awareness (starred review)

"Foolish love and flight are Ava's family inheritance. Magical realism colors this tale of a girl normal but for the wings with which she was born."
—San Francisco Chronicle

ABOUT THE AUTHOR: **Leslye Walton** has an MA in writing, and this is her first novel. Walton is a native of Tacoma, Washington, and she currently teaches middle school in Seattle.

September 2015 | Trade Paperback | Young Adult | 320 pp | $8.99 | ISBN 9780763680275
Candlewick Press | candlewick.com | leslyewalton.com

CONVERSATION STARTERS

1. The three Lavender women, Emilienne, Viviane, and Ava, all face tragedy in their lives. Discuss how each woman responds to these events. What does this say about them? Do you think the responses are fitting for the characters?

2. This novel provides a cast of many memorable characters, most of whom have strong personalities, as well as unusual names. What do the supporting characters — Cardigan Cooper, Wilhelmina Dovewolf, Marigold Pie, René Roux, Gabe — bring to the story? What role do they play, both for the main characters and in the plot?

3. Would the people of Pinnacle Lane have accepted Ava had she not been attacked, or was the horror of what happened to her necessary for them to accept her? In other words, is empathy necessary for acceptance?

4. Wilhelmina says, "Just because love don't look the way you think it should, don't mean you don't have it" (243). How does Emilienne interpret this? Do you agree with Wilhelmina?

5. Do you think what happened to Nathaniel at the end was justified? Would you have preferred a more traditional, or perhaps less obtuse, form of punishment?

6. The ending has caused much debate among readers. What do you think happened? Did Ava finally allow herself to fly, or did she succumb to those dark thoughts in the end?

7. Discuss two of the themes in the novel. How do they interact and build upon each other throughout the novel?

8. The novel begins with Emilienne's story and continues to Viviane's before leading into Ava's. What do you think about this format? How does this structure contribute to the reader's experience, as well as impact the overall plot?

9. The novel is set in a fictitious neighborhood in Seattle, Washington. How does the main setting contribute to the mood of the story? What role does the setting play in the plot?

10. Discuss the use of language throughout the story. What does the French vocabulary add to the story?

THE THING ABOUT JELLYFISH
Ali Benjamin

2015 BEA Buzz Book

2015 Publishers Lunch Buzz Book

A stunning debut about how grief can open the world in magical ways.

After her best friend dies in a drowning accident, Suzy is convinced that the true cause of the tragedy was a rare jellyfish sting. Retreating into a silent world of imagination, she crafts a plan to prove her theory—even if it means traveling the globe, alone. Suzy's achingly heartfelt journey explores life, death, the astonishing wonder of the universe...and the potential for love and hope right next door.

*"A painful story smartly told, Benjamin's first solo novel has appeal well beyond a middle school audience." —***Kirkus Reviews**, starred review

"Reminiscent of works by Jennifer L. Holm and Sharon Creech, Benjamin's novel is a shining example of the highs and lows of early adolescence." —**Publishers Weekly**, starred review

*"Seventh-grade narrator Suzy Swanson will win readers' hearts as she silently struggles to come to terms with her complex emotions over the death of her former best friend." —***Shelf Awareness**

ABOUT THE AUTHOR: **Ali Benjamin** grew up outside New York City, in a rickety old house that neighbors thought was haunted. As a child she spent countless hours catching bugs and frogs; *The Thing About Jellyfish* emerged from her fascination with the natural world. She is the cowriter of HIV-positive teen Paige Rawl's coming-of-age memoir *Positive*, as well as Tim Howard's bestseller *The Keeper*. She is a member of New England Science Writers. She lives in rural Massachusetts with her husband, two kids, and Australian shepherd named Mollie.

September 2015 | Hardcover | Young Adult | 352 pp | $17.00 | ISBN 9780316380867
Little, Brown Books for Young Readers | lb-kids.com | alibenjamin.com

CONVERSATION STARTERS

1. How does the scientific method affect how Suzy deals with Franny's death? How does it guide the structure of the novel?

2. After Franny dies, Suzy decides to start "*not-talking*." She claims, "In the end, not-talking means the same thing, more or less, as small talk. Nothing." What brings Suzy to this conclusion? Do you agree or disagree with it?

3. While researching jellyfish, Suzy learns about real-life long-distance swimmer Diana Nyad, who attempted to swim from Cuba to Florida four times only to be forced to stop due to jellyfish stings; she eventually succeeded on her fifth attempt. How does Diana's perseverance relate to Suzy's quest to prove a jellyfish stung Franny? How does it differ from it?

4. At the beginning of the novel, Suzy dismisses her classmate Sarah as a mean, popular girl and her classmate Justin as a messy rule-breaker. How do her opinions of them change and become more complex?

5. Right before Franny dies, Suzy slips frozen urine into her locker to "send a signal" that she has become a bad person. What else could Suzy have done to reach out to Franny? Do you think they could have become friends again?

6. How does what Dr. Legs describes as "your own truth" differ from what Suzy sees as "*the* truth"? Are those concepts equivalent in your mind, or are they separate?

7. Why do you think author Ali Benjamin chooses not to have Suzy make it to Australia? Are you disappointed that you didn't get to meet the character Dr. Jamie Seymour? What may have happened if Suzy had succeeded in her quest?

8. Jellyfish are amazing creatures! What did you learn about jellyfish from reading this book? What is "the thing" about jellyfish for Suzy? What significance do jellyfish now hold for you?

THIS IS WHERE IT ENDS
Marieke Nijkamp

10:00 am: The principal of Opportunity High School in Alabama finishes her speech, welcoming the entire student body to a new semester and encouraging them to excel and achieve.

10:02 am: The students get up to leave the auditorium for their next class.

10:03 am: The auditorium doors won't open.

10:05 am: Someone starts shooting.

This explosive, emotional, page-turning debut about a high school held hostage is told over fifty-four minutes from the perspective of four teens—each with their own reason to fear the boy with the gun.

"This novel will break your heart and leave you on the edge of your seat wondering what happens next . . . A hard novel to read, but This Is Where It Ends *will stay with you for a long time to come. This novel is going to be huge, just watch."* —**Dalene Kolb, Mystery Ink Bookstore (Huntington Beach, CA)**

"Well-developed characters in a story that takes place in just the span of an hour. Ending is brutal but still hopeful. An intense, riveting read." —**Kris Hickey, Columbus Metropolitan Library**

"The view from inside of a shooting is a new & much needed perspective. A must read!" —**Jennifer Demas, Fort Worth Library**

"Good heavens, this was good." —**Jami Harrison, Central Arkansas Library System**

ABOUT THE AUTHOR: **Marieke Nijkamp** is a civil servant in the Netherlands. She is an executive member of We Need Diverse Books, the founder of DiversifYA, and a founding contributor to YA Misfits. Visit her at mariekenijkamp.com.

January 2016 | Hardcover | Young Adult | 288 pp | $17.99 | ISBN 9781492622468
Sourcebooks Fire | sourcebooks.com | mariekenijkamp.com

CONVERSATION STARTERS

MARIEKE NIJKAMP

this is where it ends

1. There are many different kinds of relationships in this novel: family, friendship, romantic. How do these relationships inform what is at stake for each of the main characters?

2. Each character reacts differently to the shooting. Choose two characters and describe how they responded. Do you agree with the decisions they made? How might you have acted differently?

3. *This is Where it Ends* is interspersed with texts, social media posts, and blog excerpts. How do you think technology has affected the way we experience and respond to tragedy?

4. Autumn and Sylv keep secrets from each other. Do you think this helps or hurts their relationship? Do you agree with their decisions or would you have encouraged them to speak up?

5. Autumn doesn't feel as if she belongs in Opportunity. She tells Sylv, "If I stay here, I don't think I'll matter." What does she mean by this?

6. Early in the novel, Tomás has the opportunity to escape the school. Instead, he chooses to try to help his classmates. Discuss Tomás's decision. What would you have done?

7. Claire and Chris feel helpless as they wait for news about what is happening inside the school. In your opinion, was it more difficult for the characters inside the auditorium or those waiting to hear about their loved ones? Why?

8. Tyler told his father he wanted to go back to school to "set things right." Discuss his motivations. How could he have gone about this differently?

9. In the epilogue, the survivors come together to remember those they lost by sending lanterns into the sky. Mei describes this as a way to "make sure the darkness is never absolute." What does that mean to you?

10. What do you think happens to the survivors after the book ends? What would come next for them? How do you think their experiences changed them?

THIS RAGING LIGHT
Estelle Laure

Can the best thing happen at the worst time?

For seventeen-year-old Lucille Bennett, life currently feels like the worst joke ever. With her parents MIA, Lucille has a nine-year-old sister to care for, stacks of bills to pay, and inquisitive neighbors and teachers to avoid. This isn't the right time to fall in love.

But love—messy, complicated love—is what Lucille finds with Digby Jones, her best friend's brother. He offers Lucille a series of perfect moments during a string of seemingly impossible days. Digby's kindness—and the kindness of others around her—make Lucille realize that "maybe when a lot of bad things happen, good things have to happen too."

With blazing longing that builds to a fever pitch, Estelle Laure's soulful debut will keep readers hooked and hoping until the very last page.

"This Raging Light *is a funny, poetic, big-hearted reminder that life can— and will—take us all by surprise sometimes."* —**Jennifer E. Smith, author of *The Statistical Probability of Love at First Sight***

"Laure's characters mimic her writing, at once visceral and brave, unafraid to confront love in its every facet—surprising, surpassing, flawed. This book is a thick quilt in a cold room, and I want to wrap myself in it." —**David Arnold, author of *Mosquitoland***

"I loved this book. I was torn between wanting to devour it in one breathless read and needing to stop and savor each gorgeous turn of phrase. This is a remarkable debut." —**Morgan Matson, author of *Amy & Roger's Epic Detour* and *Since You've Been Gone***

About the Author: The debut author **Estelle Laure** is a Vonnegut worshiper who believes in love, magic, and the power of facing hard truths. She has a BA in theater arts and an MFA from Vermont College of Fine Arts in writing for children and young adults. She lives with her two children in Taos, New Mexico.

December 2015 | Hardcover | Young Adult | 288 pp | $17.99 | ISBN 9780544534292
HMH Books for Young Readers | hmhco.com | estellelaure.com

CONVERSATION STARTERS

1. What does it mean to be a teenager like Lucille, forced to take on adult responsibilities as she's coming into her own?

2. How do Lucille's parents' actions affect Lucille and Wren? Beyond the obvious negative effects, is there anything positive that comes from their circumstances?

3. Lucille's job at Fred's is more than just a paycheck to Lucille. What does she gain from her experience at her job?

4. At one point in the novel, Lucille asks the question: "Who is this boy I've known for most of always, and why is he everything?" Why is Digby so important to Lucille at this stage in her life?

5. How does Wren cope in the absence of a mother in this story?

6. How do you feel about Lucille's actions in pursuing Digby in the novel? What was your response to Digby's infidelity?

7. How would you describe Lucille's voice in the story? Did you find the first person present tense effective?

8. Discuss the role of Lucille and Wren's neighbors in the second half of the story. How did Lucille's response to their actions differ from Wren's?

9. Eden doesn't support Lucille's crush on Digby. Why is that?

10. Lucille is a victim of circumstances outside of her control. How does she take control of her destiny by the end of the novel?

UNTIL WE MEET AGAIN
Renee Collins

They exist in two different centuries, but their love defies time.

Cassandra craves drama and adventure, so the last thing she wants is to spend her summer marooned with her mother and stepfather in a snooty Massachusetts shore town. But when a dreamy stranger shows up on their private beach claiming it's his own—and that the year is 1925—she is swept into a mystery a hundred years in the making.

As she searches for answers in the present, Cassandra discovers a truth that puts their growing love—and Lawrence's life—into jeopardy. Desperate to save him, Cassandra must find a way to change history...or risk losing Lawrence forever.

"Time stood still as I read this breathtakingly beautiful story. I didn't want it to end." —**Kasie West, author of** *The Fill-In Boyfriend* **and** *The Distance Between Us*

"A beach house, a mystery, and time-travel love make Until We Meet Again *a romantic, engaging read."* —**Deb Caletti, National Book Award Finalist for** *Honey, Baby, Sweetheart*

"Moonlight, mystery, and murder make for a thrilling combination in this lush tale that bridges the present day with the Gatsby era on a time-crossed beach. Until We Meet Again *is tragically beautiful with twists you won't see coming."* —**Martina Boone, author of** *Compulsion* **and the Heirs of Watson Island trilogy**

About the Author: **Renee Collins** grew up on a beach in Hawaii. Sadly, she never met anyone from the past on those shores, but she did go on to get a degree in history, which is almost the same. She currently lives in Colorado with her family. Visit her at reneecollinsauthor.com.

November 2015 | Hardcover | Young Adult | 336 pp | $16.99 | ISBN 9781492621164
Sourcebooks Fire | sourcebooks.com

CONVERSATION STARTERS

1. Both Cassandra and Lawrence were struggling with something at the beginning of the book. Did they find resolutions by the end? In what ways did each character grow?

2. What similarities do Lawrence and Cassandra share in spite of the nearly hundred years that separate them? What are some of their differences?

3. Why was Cassandra so reluctant to tell Lawrence anything about the future? Should she have told him more?

4. Did Lawrence love Fay? Was she true competition for Cassandra?

5. Was Lawrence destined to die? Or do you think meeting Cassandra contributed to that? Did her actions in trying to save Lawrence actually seal his fate? Do you think things would have become deadly with Ned and his shady business deals no matter what?

6. Do you think Cassandra could have done something different in her efforts to save Lawrence? What would you have done in her shoes?

7. The transformative power of love is a major theme in the novel. How did Lawrence and Cassandra's love for each other transform them?

8. What do you think Cassandra meant when she told Lawrence, "Love is its own reason," near the end of the story?

9. If it had been possible to travel into each other's time, should the characters have done so? What sacrifices would they have had to make to adjust to each other's worlds? Who would it have been harder for?

10. If you could meet and fall in love with someone from another time, which era would you choose?

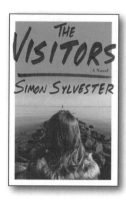

THE VISITORS
Simon Sylvester

In the tradition of Neil Gaiman and Iain Banks, Simon Sylvester brings an ancient myth to life with this lush, atmospheric coming-of-age tale.

Nobody comes to the remote Scottish island of Bancree, and seventeen-year-old Flora can't wait to move to the mainland when she finishes school. So when a mysterious man and his daughter, Ailsa, move into isolated Dog Cottage, Flora is curious. What could have brought these strangers to the island?

Meanwhile, several of the men on Bancree have disappeared, unnerving the community. When a body washes ashore, suspicion turns to the newcomers. But Flo suspects something else, even though it seems impossible. She asks local residents for anything they know about "selkies," the mythical women who can turn from seal to human and back again.

Convinced of her new neighbors' innocence, Flo is fiercely determined to protect her friend Ailsa. Can the answer to the disappearances, and to the pull of her own heart, lie out there, beyond the waves?

"Fantastic descriptions of island life, of the diesel-spluttering ferry that forms Brancree's tenuous connection with the rest of the world and of the moods of the sea around it. Lovely . . . Sylvester has a gift for storytelling."
—Sam Jordison, *The Guardian*

*"A contemporary twist on an old fisherman's myth complete with an immensely atmospheric setting, a strong yet sympathetic central character and a missing persons mystery that'll keep you guessing till all is said and done—and then some—*The Visitors *has everything including the girl going for it . . . An astonishingly assured debut."* **—Tor.com**

About the Author: **Simon Sylvester** is a writer, teacher, and occasional filmmaker. After working as a camera assistant and journalist, he began writing fiction, and his short stories are published regularly in literary journals. He lives in Cumbria with his partner and their daughter.

December 2015 | Trade Paperback | Fiction | 368 pp | $18.95 | ISBN 9781612194639
Melville House Books | mhpbooks.com | simonsylvester.wordpress.com

CONVERSATION STARTERS

1. How does starting the novel with Richard's departure set the tone for introducing us to Flora's life in Bancree? How does abandonment and loss play into the lives of Flora and Ailsa as well as the novel's larger plot?

2. In what way does the setting play a role in the story? Early critics highlighted the novel's evocative portrait of Bancree— how do characters seem to relate to the island, and how are the events that take place in the novel shaped by it?

3. The novel is also about changing, growing up, and leaving. Besides the narrator, Flo, which character seems to change the most over the course of the story? How does changing tie into the selkie stories Flo hears—and what distinction does the novel make between changing and revealing existing character traits?

4. What about selkie mythology do you think captivates Flora? Were there parts that hooked you, too?

5. Why do you think some of the selkie tales are narrated differently than the rest of the novel? Does any coherent picture of selkies emerge, or are Izzy and John's stories ultimately irreconcilable?

6. How do the string of disappearances both act as a cause and work as a figurative metaphor for Bancree's economic decline? Even after the case is solved, why do you think the overall decline isn't abetted?

7. Flora becomes disenchanted with selkie folklore after she realizes that "The selkie myth was a suppression of female sexuality" (pg. 270). How does the ending work to change this? Does it succeed?

8. What seems to be the role of the epilogue, and what sort of information is disclosed there? Why might there be an epilogue instead of, say, another chapter?

9. *The Visitors* places an emphasis on storytelling, recounting myths and reinterpreting them. Ultimately the book introduces two conflicting points of view regarding storytelling: Izzy, who believes that myths should be recounted orally, and Flo, who writes down Izzy's and other storytellers' tales. Given this divergence of viewpoints, how does *The Visitors* seem to juggle what we do with stories? What shapes Izzy's and Flo's views about stories?

BOOK GROUP FAVORITES

In 2015, we asked thousands of book groups to tell us what books they read and discussed during 2014 that they enjoyed most. The top titles were:

1. *Orphan Train* by Christina Baker Kline

2. *All the Light We Cannot See* by Anthony Doerr

3. *The Invention of Wings* by Sue Monk Kidd

4. *The Light Between Oceans* by M.L. Stedman

5. *Me Before You* by Jojo Moyes

6. *Unbroken* by Laura Hillenbrand

7. *The Goldfinch* by Donna Tartt

8. *The Storied Life of A.J. Fikry* by Gabrielle Zevin

9. *The Boys in the Boat* by Daniel James Brown

10. *Gone Girl* by Gillian Flynn

11. *The Paris Architect* by Charles Belfoure

Please visit ReadingGroupChoices.com between January 1 and April 1, 2016 to enter our 2015 Favorite Books Contest by telling us about your favorite books of 2015. You will be entered for a chance to win bookstore gift certificates to use towards your meetings plus books for each person in your group, compliments of our publishing partners.

GUIDELINES FOR LIVELY BOOK DISCUSSIONS

1. RESPECT SPACE - Avoid "crosstalk" or talking over others.

2. ALLOW SPACE - Some of us are more outgoing and others more reserved. If you've had a chance to talk, allow others time to offer their thoughts as well.

3. BE OPEN - Keep an open mind, learn from others, and acknowlege there are differences in opinon. That's what makes it interesting!

4. OFFER NEW THOUGHTS - Try not to repeat what others have said, but offer a new perspective.

5. STAY ON THE TOPIC - Contribute to the flow of conversation by holding your comments to the topic of the book, keeping personal references to an appropriate medium.

Great Books ⌒ Great People ⌒ Great Conversation

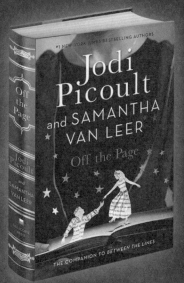

DO YOU LOVE TO READ?

Spread the joy of reading and build a sense of community by starting a Little Free Library book exchange!

Hailed by the *New York Times* as "a global sensation", Little Free Library book exchanges are "take a book, return a book" gathering places where neighbors share their favorite literature and stories.

LITTLE FREE LIBRARY.org ®
TAKE A BOOK • RETURN A BOOK

Find locations near you and learn how to start your own at *www.littlefreelibrary.org*

READING GROUP CHOICES' ADVISORY BOARD

Charlie Mead owned and managed Reading Group Choices from 2005 until 2014. He sold the business to Mary Morgan in April 2014. Charlie's business partner and wife, Barbara Drummond Mead, co-owned and managed the business until her passing in 2011. From 1972 to 1999, Charlie served at Digital Equipment Corporation (DEC) and Compaq Computer Corporation, both now part of Hewlett Packard, most recently as vice president of communication accounts worldwide. In 1999, Charlie became vice president of Sales of Interpath Communications Corporation, an Internet infrastructure company, until the company's sale in 2000. From 2000 to 2005, Charlie owned and managed Connxsys LLC, a communications consulting firm.

Donna Paz Kaufman founded Reading Group Choices in 1994 to connect publishers, booksellers, libraries, and readers with great books for group discussion. Today, the bookstore training and consulting group of Paz & Associates is fully dedicated to assisting people around the globe open, manage, and sell their independent bookstores. To learn more about Paz & Associates, visit PazBookBiz.com.

Mark Nichols was an independent bookseller in various locations from Maine to Connecticut from 1976 through 1993. After seven years in a variety of positions with major publishers in New York and San Francisco, he joined the American Booksellers Association in 2000, and currently serves as Development Officer. He is on the Board of James Patterson's ReadKiddoRead.com, and has edited two volumes with Newmarket Press—*Book Sense Best Books* (2004) and *Book Sense Best Children's Books* (2005).

John Mutter is editor-in-chief of *Shelf Awareness*, the daily e-mail newsletter focusing on books, media about books, retailing and related issues to help booksellers, librarians and others do their jobs more effectively. Before he and his business partner, Jenn Risko, founded the company in May 2005, he was executive editor of bookselling at *Publishers Weekly*. He has covered book industry issues for 25 years and written for a variety of publications, including *The Bookseller* in the U.K.; *Australian*

Bookseller & Publisher; *Boersenblatt*, the German book trade magazine; and *College Store Magazine* in the U.S. For more information about *Shelf Awareness*, go to its website, shelf-awareness.com.

Megan Hanson's background includes extensive customer service work, experience coordinating marketing campaigns for the Madrid-based NGO Colegas, plus serving as a Community Literacy Coordinator for the Madison non-profit Literacy Network. Since 2012, she has been working for the internationally-recognized non-profit Little Free Library, helping them to develop and scale to meet demand. Her focus is on digital marketing, data and web management, product development and customer service. Most recently, she co-founded the Madison chapter of the Awesome Foundation and spends her spare time freelancing on web design and digital marketing projects.

Nancy Olson owned and operated Quail Ridge Books & Music in Raleigh, NC from 1981 until it was sold in 2013. The shop has grown from 1,200 sq. ft. to 9,000+ sq. ft and sales of $3 million. The bookstore won three major awards in 2001: *Publishers Weekly* Bookseller of the Year, Charles Haslam Award for Excellence in Bookselling; Pannell Award for Excellence in Children's Bookselling. It was voted "Best in the Triangle" in the *Independent Weekly* and *Metro Magazine*.

Nicole Sullivan opened BookBar in 2013. Now in it's 3rd year, the store is undergoing a major expansion, nearly doubling in size. Nicole is also in the process of opening an author bed and breakfast above the store for visiting authors and book lovers. Sullivan is also the founder of bookclubhub.org, a reader to book club matching website. She and her team are dedicated to creating successful book store models and solutions.

Jill A. Tardiff is Chair and Event Manager of National Reading Group Month (NRGM), a marketing initiative fostered by the Women's National Book Association (WNBA), a professional development and literacy outreach nonprofit organization. She is WNBA's Main NGO Representative at the United Nations Department of Public Information and its Social Media Manager. Jill was the Association's National President (2004-2006) and the New York City Chapter's President (2000-2006).

ORDER YOUR COPIES OF READING GROUP CHOICES!

HOW MANY COPIES OF EACH EDITION WOULD YOU LIKE TO RECEIVE?

___ 2016 ___ 2015 ___ 2014 ___ 2013 ___ 2012 ___ 2011 ___ 2010 ___ 2008 ___ 2006 ___ 2005 ___ 2004

PRICING:

☐ 1-4 copies = $7.95/copy
☐ 5-24 copies = $4.75/copy
☐ 25 or more = $3.95/copy

SHIPPING & HANDLING:

☐ $2.50 for up to 5 copies
☐ $5.00 for 6-10 copies
☐ $7.50 for 11-20 copies
☐ $10.00 for over 20 copies

WI RESIDENTS:

☐ 5.5% sales tax

TOTAL COST OF COPIES: _____ + **COST OF SHIPPING:** _____ + **TAX IF APPLICABLE:** _____ = **TOTAL:** _____

PAYMENT:

☐ Check enclosed   ☐ Credit Card (VISA, MC, Discover)

Card Number _____ Exp Date _____

Signature _____

PLEASE MAIL FORM TO: Reading Group Choices • 113 Bascom Pl • Madison, WI 53726

FOR MORE INFO: info@ReadingGroupChoices.com